CALL YOURSELF
A BLUES FAN?

THE ULTIMATE
CHELSEA
QUIZ BOOK

DEDICATION

This book is for long-time Chelsea fans of my acquaintance: Doug Brown, Ben Darnton, Wayne Maddams, John Shaw, Nick Tilt and Alan Watson.

ACKNOWLEDGEMENTS

My thanks again to Stuart Tibber and Michelle Grainger for their assistance in producing this book

RACING POST

CALL YOURSELF A BLUES FAN?

THE ULTIMATE
CHELSEA
QUIZ BOOK

MART MATTHEWS

First published by Pitch Publishing on behalf of Racing Post, 2022

Pitch Publishing
Pitch Publishing,
9 Donnington Park,
85 Birdham Road,
Chichester,
West Sussex, PO20 7AJ

www.pitchpublishing.co.uk
info@pitchpublishing.co.uk
www.racingpost.com/shop

A CIP catalogue record is available for this book
from the British Library.

ISBN 9781839501012

Typesetting and origination by Pitch Publishing

Printed and bound by TJ Books Limited

CONTENTS

INTRODUCTION

Hello Chelsea fans everywhere and welcome to what I hope is the most comprehensive quiz on your club in existence. I expect my inclusions and omissions will produce some argument, particularly where my choice of 'Fulham Road Favourites' is concerned, but that's all to the good. The League Cup has had so many sponsors that I've simplified things by always referring to it as 'The League Cup'. You will find no mention of Super Cups, Club World Championships, Club World Cups, Intercontinental Cups and their like. To me they are pointless excesses that have no meaning, are usually arranged a few thousand miles from where the supporters of the clubs live and leave a carbon footprint much larger than their value in players' and supporters' lives. They fill me with as much joy as international friendlies.

QUIZ No. 1

ANYTHING GOES

1. Ron Tindall, Chelsea's centre-forward who scored 67 goals in 160 games for the club between 1955 and 1961, also played in 172 first-class cricket matches for which county?

2. Who are the only club that Chelsea have both won and lost the Community Shield against in a penalty shoot-out?

3. Chelsea were involved in a Boxing Day encounter full of incident in 2007 with three players being sent off and the visitors making it 4-4 with a last-minute penalty. Who were those visitors?

4. Chelsea were certainly up for it when Spurs came to Stamford Bridge on the night of 2 May 2016, although the home side quickly found themselves two goals down. If Chelsea could get something from the game they would snuff out any lingering hopes Spurs had of winning the Premier League. It proved enough motivation and with the help of a magnificent goal from Hazard the game ended 2-2. It wasn't pretty, however. How many yellow cards did Spurs receive that night?

5. What was unique about the goal Christian Pulisic scored for Chelsea in the 2020 FA Cup final against Arsenal?

6. Who scored a hat-trick when Chelsea won 5-1 at MK Dons in the FA Cup fourth round of the 2015/16 season?

7. On 20 November 2011 Chelsea lost 2-1 at home to Liverpool. Chelsea's goal was scored by a player who eventually joined Liverpool and the visitor's winner in the 87th minute came from someone who had previously played for Chelsea. Who were the two players?

8. Chelsea players Harold Halse and Dennis Wise are part of a club that has only five members. The other three are Ernie Taylor, John Barnes and David James. What links them all?

9. On 26 September 1970 Chelsea had a slice of luck when they beat Ipswich Town 2-1 at Stamford Bridge. A shot hit the stanchion and rebounded out but the referee gave a goal, although the shot had gone wide. Who 'scored' the goal?

10. A legendary figure because of his size, which goalkeeper played for Chelsea 34 times in their first league season after gaining one England cap and appearing in three FA Cup finals in four years for Sheffield United?

QUIZ No. 2

ASSORTED BLUES

1. Which member of Chelsea's title-winning side of 1954/55 later won the FA Cup as a manager with West Ham United?

2. Without the First World War this excellent centre-forward would have played more than the 99 matches he managed for Chelsea. He would certainly have been crowing about being the only Chelsea scorer in each of the first four games of the 1921/22 season. Who was he?

3. Which member of Chelsea's League Cup-winning side of 1965 was transferred to Birmingham City the following season after 160 league appearances for the club?

4. This scorer of the winning goal in extra time at Newcastle United in 1915 that got Chelsea into the FA Cup semi-final was a well respected member of the eventual FA Cup finalists that season and played in 222 league games for the club. If he got fed up with dashing down the wing he could always produce cars for a living! Who was he?

5. He impressed as a schoolboy at Charlton before signing for Chelsea in 1963 after over 130 games for the club from the south east of the capital. A classy centre-half who always seemed to have time on the ball, he went on to play 265 league games for the Blues. Who was he?

6. This centre-forward was the first man to score 100 league goals for the club after that earlier goalscorer George Hilsdon got stuck on 98. Between 1929 and the Second World War he turned out 220 times in the league for Chelsea and also scored a hat-trick on his England debut. Who was he?

7. But for the Second World War, this winger, who scored 62 goals in 221 league games for Chelsea, would have clocked up far more. He was still there after the War and became the oldest player to appear for the Londoners when he ran out against Bolton Wanderers in September 1947 at the age of 39. Who was he?

8. This Scotsman was as versatile as they come and was employed as a destructive midfielder in the successful Chelsea sides of the mid-to-late 1960s. He could also play a bit too. He ended his time at Chelsea just two short of 200 league appearances. Who was he?

9. Chelsea's wartime captain and a key member of their title-winning 1954/55 team, this centre-half played over 300 times for Chelsea and went on to manage Sheffield United in three different decades. Who was he?

10. We'll finish with another centre-half who came down from Scotland after his time with Morton and quickly became a fixture at the Bridge, eventually making 224 league appearances between 1983 and 1989 when he was sold to Charlton for more than six times what Chelsea paid for him. Who was he?

QUIZ No. 3

BLUES SEEING RED

1. On 23 November 2002 a Chelsea player was sent off in a 1-1 draw at Bolton, and another got his marching orders when Chelsea beat Liverpool 1-0 at Stamford Bridge on 17 September 2006. Both their surnames begin with a 'B'. Who were they?

2. In 2006 a Chelsea defender saw red in a 1-1 home draw with Charlton Athletic, then ten years later a Chelsea forward who shares the first letter of his surname with the earlier player was sent off in an FA Cup tie that Chelsea lost 2-0 at Everton. Who were the two offenders?

3. One Chelsea goalkeeper received a red card in a 3-1 defeat at Wigan in 2009, while another whose surname began with the same letter was dismissed in a 3-0 home defeat by Manchester City in 2016. Who were the two goalkeepers?

4. In October 2006 a Chelsea player was sent off in their 2-0 win at Reading, while on Boxing Day of 2009 another Chelsea player with the same first letter of his surname was given a red card in a 0-0 draw at Birmingham City. Who were the two players?

5. Spurs and Chelsea produced some fireworks of their own on 5 November 2006 when a Chelsea defender was sent off in a 2-1 defeat at White Hart Lane. Then in September five years later a Chelsea forward saw red when they beat Swansea City 4-1 at Stamford Bridge. The two players' surnames begin with the same letter. Who were they?

6. Which Chelsea defender picked up a red card at Old Trafford in a 1-1 draw with Manchester United on 8 May 2004?

7. Which Chelsea defender got a slightly early bath after being sent off in the 92nd minute of the derby with Fulham at Craven Cottage on 19 March 2006, which Chelsea lost 1-0?

8. Which Chelsea player got red cards away to both Sunderland and West Bromwich Albion in the 2005/06 season?

9. Which Chelsea midfielder was given a red card in added-on time in their 2-0 win at Derby County on 24 November 2007?

10. Which Chelsea forward saw red in a 0-0 home draw with Fulham on 29 September 2007?

QUIZ No. 4

A BRIDGE TOO FAR
(LOSING FA CUP SEMI-FINALS)

Chelsea have lost ten times in FA Cup semi-finals. Here are some questions about those defeats.

1. Which club, in 1932, became the first team to beat Chelsea in two FA Cup semi-finals, having previously beaten them in 1911?

2. In 1920 Chelsea lost 3-1 to eventual winners Aston Villa. The Londoners' first goal in a losing semi-final came appropriately enough from a man whose name rhymes with goal. Who was he?

3. Which club knocked Chelsea out at the semi-final stage twice in three years in 1950 and 1952?

4. In both those years the games went to a replay, necessitating four matches between the clubs that were all played on the same ground. Which one?

5. The 1960s brought successive FA Cup semi-final defeats by 2-0 from which two clubs, the first in 1965 and the second in 1966?

6. After a 30-year gap Chelsea lost another FA Cup semi-final in 1996. Who beat them on this occasion?

7. Who scored for Chelsea when they lost 2-1 to Liverpool in the 2006 FA Cup semi-final?

8. The player with the shortest surname to score in an FA Cup semi-final for Chelsea got their consolation goal when they lost to Manchester City in 2013. Who was he?

9. Leaving Wembley out of the equation, which I wish they would as a semi-final venue anyway, which is the only city where Chelsea have lost an FA Cup semi-final on two of its grounds?

10. What is the most common scoreline in Chelsea's FA Cup semi-final defeats?

QUIZ No. 5

CHELSEA IN EUROPE - 1958-72
- CLUBS

1. Chelsea played their first game in Europe in the Fairs Cup on 30 September 1958 and won 3-1 against BK Frem away from home. In which country were they playing?

2. In the Fairs Cup run of 1965/66, which club from Austria did they meet after knocking AS Roma out at the first hurdle?

3. The games against AC Milan are covered in the 'Players' section. Close on 60,000 turned up at Stamford Bridge for the second leg and I was one of that throng. To the nearest thousand, what had been the attendance figure in Italy for the first leg?

4. Which German club that had reached the Cup Winners' Cup final the previous season did Chelsea beat 3-2 on aggregate in the next round?

5. When Chelsea lost the third match 5-0 to Barcelona in the semi-final they must have been out on their feet with so many games and so much travel. They also reached the FA Cup semi-final. How many competitive matches did they play that season?

6. As related in the 'Players' section, when they returned to the tournament in 1968/69 they accounted for Morton in the first round. The next round saw 210 minutes of stalemate without a goal in sight. During this period the players seemed to spend as much time tossing coins as playing football and Chelsea weren't very good at it. Coin tossing that is, not football! Who knocked them out by this method?

7. The 1970/71 season saw them lift the European Cup Winners' Cup. After removing Aris Thessalonikis they won 1-0 home and away against CFKA Sredets. Which country did they represent?

8. The next round brought a pleasing finish for Chelsea fans at Stamford Bridge when Chelsea overturned a 2-0 deficit from the first leg to win the second leg 4-0 after extra time against which club?

9. As they had two rounds before, Chelsea won the semi-final 1-0 home and away against the holders of the trophy. Who were they?

10. After beating Real Madrid after a replay in the final Chelsea defended the trophy in 1971/72 and must have thought it would be a doddle to win it again when they defeated Jeunesse Hautcharage 21-0 on aggregate, creating a few records along the way. However, things went from the sublime to the ridiculous in the next round when they went out on the away-goals rule to Atvidaberg. From which countries did their two opponents come?

QUIZ No. 6

CHELSEA IN EUROPE – 1958-72 – PLAYERS

1. Well, who do you think scored home and away against Chelsea's first European opponents in the 1958/59 season? Have a guess.

2. It was the Inter-Cities Fairs Cup that Chelsea entered that season and in the next round they lost 4-2 on aggregate to Ville de Belgrade. Which winger scored both of their goals?

3. They had a right go at winning that trophy the next time they entered it in 1965/66, going out in the semi-final after the loss of the toss of a coin to decide the venue of the third match after the first two produced a stalemate. They had won the second leg 2-0 at Stamford Bridge against Barcelona. Which two players scored their goals?

4. In that first European adventure of the 1960s, on 22 September 1965, who became the first Chelsea player to score a hat-trick in Europe when Chelsea beat Roma 4-1 in the first leg of their first tie in the competition?

5. It wasn't only the semi-final that went to three matches. Earlier they had a titanic contest against AC Milan, losing 2-1 away and winning 2-1 at home. Which Chelsea man scored in both games?

6. Chelsea lost the coin toss for the venue of the deciding third match and had to return to Milan where not even extra time could separate the sides, but Ron Harris got this coin toss right and Chelsea went through after a 1-1 draw. Who scored that vital goal that night?

7. In 1968/69 they returned to the Fairs Cup and beat Scottish club Morton 9-3 on aggregate in the first round. Which Chelsea player found the net in both games?

8. Chelsea made quite a splash when they entered the European Cup Winners' Cup for the first time in 1970/71 and ended up winning it. When they beat Greek club Aris Thessalonikis 5-1 in the second leg at Stamford Bridge in the first round three players with surnames starting with 'H' were among the goals. Who were they?

9. In the final against Real Madrid it took two more games to decide the outcome. Who scored for Chelsea in both of them?

10. In that last match when the trophy was won 2-1, which Chelsea player scored his only goal in Europe for the club?

QUIZ No. 7

CHELSEA IN EUROPE - 1994-2000

1. It had been over 20 years since Chelsea had tasted European football when they entered the European Cup Winners' Cup in 1994/95 because FA Cup winners Manchester United had also won the league and therefore competed in the Champions League. Chelsea beat their first opponents in the competition, Viktoria Zizkov, 4-2 on aggregate. Which country were they from?

2. After accounting for Austria Wien and Bruges, they went out to Real Zaragoza in the semi-final. If they had won that semi-final which event would have happened 24 years before it did?

3. In 1997/98 Chelsea were back in the tournament and this time they won it, beating VFB Stuttgart in the final. On the way they had a 7-1 win over a Norwegian side at Stamford Bridge, running out 9-4 winners on aggregate. Who were their opponents and which Chelsea player scored five of their nine goals?

4. The other three clubs beaten by Chelsea that season were Slovan Bratislava, Real Betis and Vicenza. Di Matteo and Vialli scored in three of the nine matches they needed to win it. Who scored in four of them?

5. Chelsea made a good stab at defending the trophy the following season with three wins over Scandinavian clubs in Helsingborgs, FC Copenhagen and Valerenga before going out in the semi-final to Real Mallorca. This was the competition's final season and if Chelsea had won that semi-final they would have fancied their chances in the final due to the venue being chosen for that event. Where was it held?

6. When Chelsea were entitled to go for the inaugural European Cup competition as English champions in 1955/56, the FA forbade them to take part! Now, in the last year of the century, under a new and somewhat misleading name for it, Chelsea were at last able to test themselves against the elite, and did well in reaching the quarter final. Which Spanish club knocked them out in that quarter final?

7. In the first group stage they drew 1-1 and 0-0 with one Italian club and in the second group stage they had drawn away to another Italian club before losing to them 2-1 at Stamford Bridge in the final game of the series when a draw would have meant Chelsea had topped a group for the second time. Who were their two Italian opponents?

8. Who was Chelsea's only goalscorer from the penalty spot in the Champions League in that 1999/2000 season, his goal being the first they scored in the competition in a 2-1 defeat at Hertha Berlin?

9. In the 14-match marathon that constituted their participation in the Champions League that season, they scored 22 goals. Who, with five of them, was their top scorer in the competition?

10. Their biggest win was by 5-0 and came at Stamford Bridge in the first group stage against which Turkish club?

CALL YOURSELF A BLUES FAN?

QUIZ No. 8

CHELSEA IN EUROPE - 2000-04

1. Chelsea's first two years of UEFA Cup football in the new century were unsuccessful to say the least. Which Swiss club beat them 2-1 on aggregate at the first hurdle in 2000/01?

2. Which Chelsea player got that solitary goal in a 1-0 win at Stamford Bridge that they failed to defend in Switzerland?

3. The following season in the same competition started well enough, with a 5-0 aggregate win over Levski Sofia. Which Chelsea player scored in both legs?

4. However, it really went downhill from that point when they went out to an Israeli side in the next round and the next season lost 5-4 on aggregate at the first time of asking to a side from Norway. Which two clubs did the damage to the UEFA Cup hopes that Chelsea had?

5. In 2003/04 Chelsea got themselves back in the Champions League via a qualifier against Zilina and then went on to top their group. They won their opening group game away to Sparta Prague 1-0 with whose goal?

6. Chelsea had odd results against the Turkish club in their group, winning 2-0 away after losing 2-0 at home. Who were they playing?

7. Their most impressive performance came in a 4-0 win at Lazio and was a major contribution to winning the group. At the first knock-out stage they went through 1-0 on aggregate against a German club despite nobody in a Chelsea shirt scoring in either game, their solitary goal being an own goal. Who did they beat?

8. In the quarter-final they drew 1-1 at home in the first leg but the 2-1 away win in the second leg must have given them immense pleasure. Who did they put out of the competition?

9. The semi-final proved a bridge too far when they went down 5-3 on aggregate to which French club?

10. Their 21 goals in the Champions League were spread out to such an extent that it took just four goals to be top man in that department. Who took that accolade?

QUIZ No. 9

CHELSEA IN EUROPE - 2004-07

1. These were good years in the Champions League for Chelsea, with two semi-final appearances in 2004/05 and 2006/07. In the first of those years they opened up with wins by 3-0, 3-1 and 2-0 over PSG, Porto and CSKA Moscow. Which Chelsea player found the net in all three of those games?

2. Those early wins enabled them to top their group and in the second leg of the first knockout round they overcame a first leg 2-1 deficit against Barcelona to win 4-2 at Stamford Bridge in one of the club's greatest nights, despite two goals and a magical display from Ronaldinho. One of Barcelona's scorers in the first leg later joined Chelsea, as did the man who put through his own net for Chelsea's goal. Who were the two players?

3. Chelsea's next game in the competition was in the quarter-final first leg at Stamford Bridge and resulted in another 4-2 win, this time against Bayern Munich, which they defended successfully in the second leg in Munich. Two scorers for Bayern, one in the away leg and the other in the home leg, both later joined Chelsea. Who were the two players?

4. Chelsea met 11 clubs in the Champions League over these three seasons, but only came up against one other German club in that time. They lost and won against them in the group stage of the 2006/07 season. Who were they?

5. Only one Chelsea player scored a hat-trick in the competition over those three years and it came in a 3-1 win at Levski Sofia in the group stage of 2006/07. Who scored it?

6. In how many games over these three seasons of Champions League football did Jose Mourinho face up to his old club Porto, and was he behind, in front or level with them after those matches?

7.   After knocking Barcelona out in 2004/05 and being knocked out by them the following year, the two clubs met yet again in the group stage in 2006/07, with Chelsea winning 1-0 at home and drawing 2-2 away. In the away game one of the Barcelona goals was scored by someone who would leave for Chelsea while the other was scored by someone who had left Chelsea for Barcelona. Who were the two players?

8.   Well, it can't be put off any longer; although it was a good time for Chelsea in Europe it was marred by one other club, and that club was Liverpool. Just as with Barcelona, they met each other in each of these three seasons, playing six times in all. How many goals were scored in these six games?

9.   Who scored Chelsea's only goal against Liverpool in this period, it proving to be the winner in the first leg of the semi-final of 2006/07 at Stamford Bridge?

10. Liverpool won two Champions League semi-finals against Chelsea, in 2004/05 and 2006/07, the first with a highly dubious goal at Anfield, and the second in a penalty shoot-out on that same ground. The scorer of the goal that produced the penalty shoot-out came just short of putting a dagger to Chelsea's heart. Who was he?

QUIZ No. 10

CHELSEA IN EUROPE - 2007-10

1. In each of these three seasons Chelsea won a group match by 4-0. In 2007/08 it was away to a Danish club, the following season it was in their first game at home to a French club, and in 2009/10 it was at home to a Spanish club. Which three teams did they beat?

2. In the 2007/08 season Chelsea benefitted from an own goal in the quarter-final against a Turkish club and in the semi-final against a club a bit closer to home. They came in the away legs on each occasion and in the Turkish case the player scored at the right end as well. Which two teams played Chelsea?

3. An exciting Champions League final against Manchester United could have been won with a bit more help from the woodwork, but which two players didn't exactly cover themselves in glory, the first by being unnecessarily sent off in extra time and the second by missing the final spot kick when he eventually decided to take one after allowing John Terry to be sent up before him?

4. In the group stage of the 2008/09 campaign in the Champions League, Chelsea beat Roma 1-0 at home and lost 3-1 away. Who scored those two Chelsea goals?

5. After getting out of the group in 2008/09, Chelsea met three big names in a row, knocking out Juventus and Liverpool before going out in the semi-final to Barcelona. How many years in a row had Chelsea now met Liverpool in the Champions League and how did their quarter-final second leg at Stamford Bridge end up?

6. In Chelsea's excellent 3-1 win at Anfield in the first leg of the quarter-final, which defender came up with two of the goals and which Liverpool player who would eventually come to Stamford Bridge scored their goal?

7. Only three players scored in the Champions League for Chelsea in all these three seasons. Didier Drogba and Frank Lampard are two of them. Who is the third?

8. In the 2009/10 Champions League campaign Chelsea had three 1-0 wins in the group stage. These came home and away against Porto and in the away tie at Apoel Nicosia. One player got all three winning goals. Who was he?

9. Which former Chelsea player scored for Roma when they beat Chelsea 3-1 in a group match in Rome in 2008/09?

10. Which Italian club put paid to Chelsea's hopes of European glory by beating them 3-1 on aggregate in the first knockout round of the 2009/10 season?

CHELSEA IN EUROPE - 2010-13

1. After topping their Champions League group, Chelsea beat Copenhagen in the first knockout stage before going out in the quarter-final to which British club in 2010/11?

2. Which player scored seven of their 17 goals in the competition that season when his nearest challengers could only manage two?

3. 2011/12 was the season in which they finally landed the big one. It never looked on at any stage of the competition. In the first knockout round they trailed 3-1 after the first leg in Italy but bounced back to win the second leg 4-1 after extra time at Stamford Bridge. Which Italian club went out?

4. After removing Benfica from the scene in the quarter-final, they met Barcelona at the same semi-final stage, as they had gone out to them the previous season after the most disgusting refereeing decisions in a massive game I've ever seen. This time, after a 1-0 win in the first leg, plagued by injuries and a man down when John Terry got a red card in the second leg they somehow found the will to turn a losing position into a winning one by drawing 2-2 on the night. Who were the two scorers?

5. The final venue being Bayern Munich's home ground was another obstacle to overcome in that Allianz Arena, and it didn't look possible when the Germans went in front seven minutes from the end. Two players combined to get Chelsea's equaliser in the 88th minute, one with a perfectly flighted corner and the other by getting his head on the end of it. Who were they?

6. Which ex-Chelsea player missed an extra-time penalty for Bayern Munich when his shot was saved by Petr Čech, and who scored the decisive penalty in the shoot-out that won that elusive Champions League trophy for Chelsea at long last?

7. Chelsea failed to get out of their Champions League group in 2012/13. They lost 2-1 at Shakhtar Donetsk and then beat them 3-2 at Stamford Bridge. Which Chelsea player scored in both games and which Shakhtar Donetsk player who scored their two away goals later became a Chelsea player?

8. It's not a set up that I've got any time for but entering the Europa League halfway through the competition after exiting the Champions League certainly proved to be the perfect tonic for Chelsea when they ended up winning it by beating which club in the final?

9. Chelsea defenders enjoyed a great time when they went forward in the latter stages of the tournament. One of them scored both home and away against Rubin Kazan in the quarter-final and repeated the trick again in the semi-final against Basle. Who was he?

10. Not to be outdone, another defender also scored both home and away in that semi-final, while a third got their last-minute winner in the final itself. Who were the two men?

QUIZ No. 12

CHELSEA IN EUROPE - 2013-17

1. Which club did Chelsea knock out of the Champions League on away goals in the quarter-final in 2013/14 but get knocked out by that same club in the semi-final of 2014/15 by the same method?

2. Which German club did Chelsea play in the group stage in both 2013/14 and 2014/15, winning three and drawing one of them with a collective score of 12-1?

3. Who scored his last goal in Europe for Chelsea in a 4-0 away win over Steaua Bucharest in the group stage of the 2013/14 season?

4. In the first leg of the Champions League semi-final in 2013/14, Chelsea drew 0-0 away from home and must have felt confident about booking their place in the final. Which team came to Stamford Bridge and won 3-1 on the night to burst that particular balloon?

5. Chelsea topped their group in the Champions League in 2013/14, 2014/15 and 2015/16. However, in the first of those seasons they did so despite losing both games 2-1 and 1-0 to which club?

6. Chelsea scored six times in a game just once in Europe during this period. It happened when they beat a Slovenian club 6-0 at Stamford Bridge in the group stage in 2014/15. Who were their opponents?

7. In the group stage of 2015/16, which club did Chelsea beat 4-0 home and away?

8. Which Chelsea player scored in five of their six group matches that season?

9. Didier Drogba returned to Stamford Bridge on 18 March 2014 in the second leg of the first knockout round of the Champions League. His team lost 2-0 on the night and 3-1 on aggregate to Chelsea. Who was he playing for?

10. At what stage were Chelsea knocked out of Europe in the 2016/17 season?

QUIZ No. 13

CHELSEA IN EUROPE – 2017–21

1. Chelsea started their Champions League campaign with a flourish in 2017/18 when they won 6-0 at home to a team from Azerbaijan. They also won the away leg 4-0. Who did they beat and how many individual scorers were there in their ten goals over the two games?

2. Chelsea got out of the group but went out at the first knockout round to which club?

3. Chelsea were forced to endure the Thursday night misery that is the Europa League in 2018/19, but it didn't seem to phase them and 15 matches later the thing was back in the trophy cabinet at Stamford Bridge. Two Chelsea players scored hat-tricks along the way, the first coming in a 3-1 home win over Bate Borisov in the group stage, while the second arrived in a 5-0 away win in the second knockout round against Dynamo Kiev. Which two players landed these hat-tricks?

4. Chelsea also, unsurprisingly, won the home leg against Dynamo Kiev by 3-0. Which Chelsea player scored in both legs?

5. Which two other clubs did Chelsea beat to reach the semi-final, one from Sweden and the other from the Czech Republic?

6. Which German club did Chelsea need penalties to get past in that semi-final after two 1-1 draws?

7. Who was Chelsea's leading goalscorer in the competition with 11, and why was their 4-1 win in the final particularly pleasing for him?

8. In 2019/20 Chelsea were back in the Champions League and Stamford Bridge witnessed a crazy group match in which two Chelsea players put through their own net and Jorginho scored two penalties. The game ended in a 4-4 draw. Who was it against?

9. Chelsea's final group game saw them clinch a place in the knockout stage with a 2-1 home win over Lille. Which ex-Chelsea player scored the away side's goal?

10. After suffering a humiliating 7-1 aggregate defeat at the hands of Bayern Munich at the first knockout stage in 2019/20, Chelsea stormed back the following season to land the Champions League by beating Manchester City in the final with a goal from Havertz. Which two clubs from the same country did Chelsea eliminate in the knockout stage, and can you explain the fact that they played in Porto and didn't play in Porto during the campaign?

QUIZ No. 14

CHELSEA IN THE FA CUP FINAL - PART 1

1. Chelsea have the distinction of being the last club to win the trophy at the 'old' Wembley and the first to do so at the 'new' Wembley. True or false?

2. Which club have Chelsea lost three FA Cup finals against and never beaten in one?

3. Which one of Chelsea's 11 opponents in an FA Cup final has still not won the trophy?

4. Which two clubs from the same city have Chelsea beaten in an FA Cup final?

5. Who are the only two teams that Chelsea have both beaten and lost to in an FA Cup final?

6. Who are the only club that Chelsea have played in an FA Cup final replay?

7. The two finals of 1997 and 2009 produced incredibly fast goals. Chelsea were on the right side of it in the first instance and the victims in the second. Which two players scored those goals?

8. Chelsea have had two players sent off in the FA Cup final. The dismissals came in 2017 and 2020. Which two players saw red in more ways than one?

9. Which two clubs that Chelsea met in an FA Cup final were relegated from the top flight in the same season?

10. Who is the only player to score from the penalty spot for Chelsea in an FA Cup final?

QUIZ No. 15

CHELSEA IN THE FA CUP FINAL - PART 2

1. Which post-war player is the only man to score against Chelsea in an FA Cup final and then, three years later, play for them in one?

2. Who was the first player to score for Chelsea in an FA Cup final?

3. Which three players with surnames beginning with 'C' have scored against Chelsea in an FA Cup final?

4. After being given a torrid time at Wembley in the 1970 FA Cup final, who came up with the winner in the replay?

5. Which post-war Chelsea player has missed from the penalty spot for the Blues in an FA Cup final?

6. When Chelsea played in their first FA Cup final in 1915 against Sheffield United their opponents' surnames included an occupation and the place he works in. Who were the two players?

7. Who is the only man to score for Chelsea in an FA Cup final in two different centuries?

8. There has been just one occasion when two Chelsea players with surnames beginning with the same letter both scored for them in an FA Cup final. Who are the two players?

9. Which Chelsea manager came on as a substitute in the 1994 FA Cup final against Manchester United after 65 minutes, and who did he replace?

10. After Chelsea's electric start to the 1997 FA Cup final against Middlesbrough who made the game safe for them with the second goal?

QUIZ No. 16

CHELSEA IN THE FA CUP - 1905-39

1. In 1923 and 1924 Chelsea were eliminated from the FA Cup in successive seasons by the same club for the only time in this period. Who beat them?

2. Five other clubs knocked them out on two occasions between 1905 and 1939. One came from the North East, one from the second city, one from Wales and two from London. Can you name all five?

3. Chelsea's first experience of FA Cup football was a happy one when they won 6-1 against a military outfit at Stamford Bridge on 7 October 1905. Who did they beat?

4. Things didn't end so well in the FA Cup that first season when which London club inflicted their heaviest defeat in the competition, winning 7-1 at home to Chelsea?

5. Chelsea were knocked out by the team that went on to win it on five occasions. The years were 1915, 1920, 1927, 1930 and 1932. Who were the five FA Cup winners?

6. The most cup ties that Chelsea played against any one club over this time was seven. Which Yorkshire club were involved?

7. Chelsea were knocked out on the south coast by three clubs over this period. Which of the following clubs is the odd one out, being the one of the four that didn't meet Chelsea in the FA Cup at any time over this period? – Bournemouth, Brighton, Portsmouth and Southampton.

8. Although World War One intervened, Chelsea met the same club in the FA Cup three seasons running in 1915, 1920 and 1921. Who were they?

9. On the first day of 1908 Chelsea ran up a big score when they beat Worksop Town 9-1 in the first round. Which Chelsea front man got a double hat-trick?

10. The last cup tie Chelsea played before the war was in the quarter-final in 1939 at home to a team they beat 5-1 the week after, but lost to on the day. That club, in black and white stripes, went on to lose to Wolves in the semi-final. Who were they?

QUIZ No. 17

CHELSEA IN THE FA CUP - 1945-60

1. In the first season back after the war the FA Cup was played over two legs and Chelsea beat Leicester City 3-1 on aggregate in their first games. Which centre-forward scored their first peacetime goal in a 1-1 draw at Stamford Bridge in the first leg?

2. These were the days of marathon cup ties and Chelsea went into the record books in 1956 when they played which Lancastrians five times in the fourth round before they came out on top 2-0?

3. After no decision in the first replay, their next three attempts at a result were rather unfairly at Highbury, White Hart Lane and which other ground?

4. The only hat-trick in an FA Cup tie by a Chelsea player in this period came in a 5-1 win over Leeds United at Villa Park in a fifth-round second replay on 3 March 1952, and was scored by someone who went on to win all the major honours in the game, but not with Chelsea. Who was he?

5. Who were the only two Chelsea players to score from the penalty spot in an FA Cup tie in this period?

6. Who, with a total of 21 goals, was Chelsea's leading goalscorer in the competition during this period?

7. Who were the only club to knock Chelsea out of the FA Cup in successive years in 1959 and 1960, and were also the only club to beat them three times in the competition over this time? If you need a clue, by 1957 they had won the cup more times than any other club.

8. Which club did Chelsea play seven FA Cup ties against during the period in question?

9. Perhaps Chelsea's lowest-ever FA Cup feeling came in 1958 when, after a 3-3 draw in the fourth round at Stamford Bridge, they lost 4-1 to a club from the North East who are no longer in the league but at that time were five places from the bottom of Division Three North. Who were they?

10. In 1950 and 1954 Chelsea were knocked out by clubs that went on to win it. Which two were they?

QUIZ No. 18

CHELSEA IN CUP COMPETITIONS – 1960-70

1. Chelsea clearly hadn't learnt anything from the giant-killing they experienced in 1958 because on 3 January 1961 they were knocked out of the FA Cup by a club from the Fourth Division. Frank Blunstone scored his last FA Cup goal for Chelsea in the game against the team he started out with. Who were they?

2. Who were the only club to beat Chelsea twice in an FA Cup tie in the 1960s, winning 4-3 in 1962 in the third round, and 2-0 in the semi-final in 1965?

3. Chelsea had an odd experience in their fourth-round replay at Stamford Bridge which they won 2-1 on 3 February 1969. The match had originally been played on 29 January but with Chelsea ahead 2-0 the floodlights failed, giving their Lancastrian opponents another bite at the cherry that they failed to take. Who were those opponents?

4. Chelsea's only hat-trick in the FA Cup over this period came on 21 February 1970 on their way to winning the trophy for the first time. It came in a 4-2 win in the quarter-final against QPR at Loftus Road. Who scored it?

5. Which Chelsea player got a magnificent haul of 25 FA Cup goals over the decade?

6. Chelsea made a spectacular start to the new League Cup competition on 10 October 1960 with a 7-1 win away over another London club. Which one?

7. And it didn't stop there! On 16 November in the third round they got another seven away from home in Yorkshire. Who were their victims this time?

8. On 15 October 1969 Chelsea were knocked out of the League Cup 1-0 away on the most northerly ground they played on in either cup competition over the decade. Who beat them?

9. In the League Cup of 1966/67 Chelsea beat Charlton 5-2, drew with Blackpool 1-1 and lost to them 3-1. Which Chelsea player scored in all three games?

10. Like many clubs, Chelsea weren't sure what to make of the League Cup and entered it six times over the decade. However, it brought some magic to the club in 1964/65 when they won it. Tough question on its way! In winning it they beat Birmingham City, Notts County, Swansea Town, Aston Villa, Leicester City and one other club. This club, who are no longer in the league, were the only one they were meeting in the competition for the second time and they beat them 2-0 after a replay to reach the semi-final. Who were they?

QUIZ No. 19

CHELSEA IN CUP COMPETITIONS – 1970-80

1. Which city's two clubs put paid to Chelsea's hopes in the two domestic cup competitions in 1970/71?

2. In the 1971/72 season in which Chelsea reached the League Cup final they defeated one club in the FA Cup and the League Cup, 3-0 at home in the FA Cup and bizarrely 6-0 away after a 1-1 home draw in the League Cup. Who were they?

3. In that 6-0 away win, which Chelsea striker got a hat-trick?

4. Which London club from a lower division were the only side to beat Chelsea twice in the FA Cup over the decade, knocking them out of the competition in 1972 and 1978?

5. Which club did Chelsea beat in the League Cup semi-final of 1972 to get to Wembley and which side did they lose to in the semi-final the following season?

6. In the away second leg of the losing League Cup semi-final of 1972/73, what caused the abandonment of the original game on 20 December, necessitating it to be played again on 3 January?

7. Besides the answer to question four, which three other London clubs knocked Chelsea out of the FA Cup during this decade?

8. Chris Garland scored a hat-trick in a 4-2 home win for Chelsea in the League Cup on 2 September 1974 against which Welsh club?

9. What was odd about the scorers when Chelsea beat Burnley 6-2 in the FA Cup fourth round on 31 January 1978?

10. Which club knocked Chelsea out of the League Cup three times in four seasons?

QUIZ No. 20

CHELSEA IN CUP COMPETITIONS – 1980-90

1. Chelsea's best run in this decade was to the League Cup semi-final in 1984/85. They were beaten by a club who were relegated from the First Division that season, a fate that also befell the club they met in the final after beating Chelsea. Who were the two clubs?

2. Which Welsh club knocked Chelsea out of the League Cup in 1980/81 and 1986/87?

3. Another Welsh club took Chelsea to three games in the FA Cup fourth round in 1982 despite also experiencing relegation from Division Two at the season's end. Who were they?

4. Chelsea had their first experience of deciding a domestic cup tie by a penalty shoot-out in the League Cup at Stamford Bridge on 25 October 1983 when they won 4-3 on penalties after extra time. Chelsea had won the first leg by 2-0 away from home and then lost at home by the same score. Who were their opponents from the Midlands?

5. Chelsea played three matches in the League Cup in 1981/82. They drew 1-1 at Southampton and beat the same club 2-1 at home, and then went out 4-2 at Wigan Athletic. Which player scored for Chelsea in all three games?

6. Which Chelsea front man managed two four timers, the first in a 4-0 second-leg win over Gillingham on 13 September 1983 in the League Cup, and the second in a 5-0 win over Wigan Athletic in an FA Cup replay on 26 January 1985?

7. Chelsea scored just twice in the FA Cup in the 1985/86 season, beating Shrewsbury Town 1-0 away before losing 2-1 at home to Liverpool, the eventual winners of the trophy. Who scored both Chelsea goals?

8. Chelsea made no progress in the League Cup of 1987/88, losing to Reading on aggregate 5-4. One Chelsea man did well however by scoring all four of their goals. Who was he?

9. Which London club did Chelsea lose to in the FA Cup and beat in the League Cup in the 1984/85 season?

10. The decade ended very badly in the League Cup when Chelsea went out in successive seasons to two clubs beginning with 'S' that they had never previously played against in a cup competition, one of which they had never played before in any context. Who were the two clubs?

QUIZ No. 21

CHELSEA IN CUP COMPETITIONS – 1990-2000

1. In 1990/91 Chelsea met one club in both domestic cup competitions, going out to them 3-1 at the first hurdle in the FA Cup but beating them 2-1 away in the League Cup on their way to the semi-final. Who were they?

2. Chelsea reached the FA Cup final in 1994, although it was a big let-down on the day itself. Who, with six goals, was their leading goalscorer on the road to Wembley?

3. In 1994/95 Chelsea went out of the FA Cup on penalties in the fourth round to another club from the capital, but against their very next opponents in the following season they went through on penalties after a replay. Who were their two opponents?

4. In 1996/97, on their way to winning the trophy, Chelsea got the better of Leicester City in the fifth-round replay by 1-0, the goal coming from the penalty spot. Who scored it?

5. In a real rarity the team they beat in that 1997 FA Cup final was also the one they beat by the same score in the following year's League Cup final. Who were they?

6. It was a torturous course that Chelsea plotted to that League Cup success in 1998 when none of their four encounters against Blackburn Rovers, Southampton, Ipswich Town and Arsenal to get them to Wembley were decided in normal time. The first and last of them went to penalties. What was odd about the outcome?

7. As the decade drew towards its close, which Chelsea player scored a hat-trick at Stamford Bridge against Aston Villa in the first match of their League Cup campaign of 1998/99, a game they won 4-1?

8. Another hat-trick hero appeared in the following season in the shape of Gus Poyet. His goals came in a 6-1 away win in the FA Cup third round of 1999/2000 against which club?

9. Chelsea went on to win the FA Cup again that season, but Chelsea's hoodoo club in the competition in this decade was Manchester United. How many times did they knock Chelsea out?

10. Perhaps Chelsea's greatest performance in either competition over the decade came at Highbury against Arsenal in the League Cup of 1998/99. What score did they win by?

QUIZ No. 22

CHELSEA IN LEAGUE CUP FINALS (UP TO AND INCLUDING 2022)

1. Which goalkeeper played against Chelsea in League Cup finals for two different clubs?

2. Who is the only player to score for Chelsea in a League Cup final with a 'Z' in his name?

3. Which three defenders have all scored for Chelsea in a League Cup final, the goals coming in the finals of 1965, 1998 and 2015?

4. Who is the only man to score against Chelsea in a League Cup final from the penalty spot?

5. Which five players have found the net for Chelsea in both a League Cup final and an FA Cup final?

6. Who are the only two clubs that Chelsea have met twice in a League Cup final?

7. In Chelsea's first League Cup final in 1965 the outcome was decided over two legs with Chelsea winning 3-2 on aggregate. Who did they beat?

8. On three occasions a League Cup final in which Chelsea were playing was decided in extra time. What was Chelsea's win and lose record in those three matches?

9. Which two clubs have Chelsea played against in League Cup finals that were decided by a penalty shoot-out?

10. Which club have Chelsea beaten by the same score in both a League Cup final and an FA Cup final?

QUIZ No. 23

CHELSEA IN THE LEAGUE - 1905-39

1. Chelsea's first season in league football of 1905/06 brought a stack of goals for the home fans as they registered six goals against Barnsley, Blackpool and Clapton Orient. They went one better on 3 March 1906 when they beat a club beginning with a 'B' 7-0 at Stamford Bridge. This club left the league two years later but returned after the war minus the original first word of their name. Who were they?

2. After a third-place finish in that first season, promotion was attained in the second. What was unique to this whole period about Chelsea's home record over 19 games in that 1906/07 season?

3. Having got up they struggled to hold on to their elevated status and went down again in 1909/10. In the following season they looked set to go straight back up but lost four of their last five games and lost out. This season was the only one in this period where they remained unbeaten at home. What was their excellent record in those 19 matches?

4. In 1911/12 they had the opposite experience in the last few key games, winning their last four to pip Burnley and go up with Derby County, but life was tough in the top flight and they avoided relegation that first season back by winning their final three games, sending Notts County down instead. Which Chelsea player scored in each of those games, netting a hat-trick in the final one?

5. Chelsea flirted with relegation too closely again in the final pre-war season of 1914/15 and finished in the bottom two, along with Spurs. What was unique about Chelsea's away record in this season?

6. Chelsea's misery at yet another relegation didn't materialise because at the end of the war the league was extended and not only did they keep their place at the top table, but they had also assembled an excellent side to finish in their highest position in the top flight thus far. Where did they finish in that 1919/20 season?

7. Chelsea blew hot and cold in the 1920s. On more than one occasion they won seven league games in a row yet they often struggled too. In 1922/23 they finished two places above the trap door when they frustrated their home fans by creating a record number of draws in the 21 Stamford Bridge encounters. How many did they draw?

8. The reprieve didn't last long and they were relegated again in 1923/24. It was typical of them that after failing to score in 22 matches and going on a run of one win in 17 games that sealed their fate, they won the season's last four games when it was all too late! Promotion eluded them despite several promising situations over the next five seasons before they finally got over the line again in 1929/30, going up as runners-up to which Lancastrian club?

9. Chelsea clung on to their newly won status throughout the 1930s, sometimes comfortably and sometimes not. In 1934/35, when they finished 12th, the Stamford Bridge crowd were treated to some goalscoring heroics by two players. One of them scored four times at home to Liverpool and three against Blackburn Rovers, while the other rattled in four against both Leeds United and Manchester City. Who were the two players?

10. As Auden's 'dishonest decade' came to its close with the prospect of war looming large, Chelsea found themselves in another spot of bother. After looking likely to end that 1938/39 season just under halfway, they lost five in a row in April and found themselves involved in the dog fight at the bottom. They escaped by one point in the end to go into the war years with their Division One status intact. Their survival was largely down to one man who scored in all their last six games of the season when nobody else found the net at all. His goal in the 1-1 home draw with Birmingham effectively sent them down and kept Chelsea up. Who was he?

QUIZ No. 24

CHELSEA IN THE LEAGUE - 1946-60

1. Chelsea's return to peacetime football was not without its problems, with the defence conceding seven at Liverpool and six at both Stoke City and Wolves. They finished an inglorious 15th, but which player got a hat-trick in a 4-1 away win at Huddersfield Town on 14 December 1946?

2. Which Chelsea player in 1947/48 was the only ever-present in the league, the joint-top league goalscorer and the only Chelsea player to score a hat-trick, which came in a 4-1 home win over Stoke City on 15 November 1947?

3. Chelsea looked odds-on to experience another relegation in 1950/51 but won their last four games at the death to end up on 32 points with two other clubs, one from Merseyside and the other from Yorkshire. The Blues survived on goal average at the expense of which two clubs?

4. There followed two more nail biting seasons in 19th place, in the second of which they needed to beat a northern side at Stamford Bridge to avoid the drop. Who did they beat 3-1 on 29 April 1953?

5. The next season saw an improvement to eighth place, but nobody could have expected what happened next as they took the title for the first time in their Golden Jubilee season of 1954/55. The players in the No. 6 and No. 7 shirts never missed a match all season. Who were they?

6. It didn't seem remotely possible when, after a terrible October that saw them take one point from a possible ten, they had lost more games than they had won after 17 fixtures. Not that they cared, but those early reverses meant that they equalled the record for the lowest points total by league champions since the inception of the 42-match programme in the 1919/20 season. Their total of 52 points was matched by Arsenal when they won it in 1938 and by another club in 1929. This other club was also the one that Chelsea clinched the title against, with their 3-0 win at Stamford Bridge on 23 April 1955. Who were they?

7. It was a case of 'after the Lord Mayor's show' the following season, their drop from champions to 16th being the biggest since which club was relegated in 1937/38 after winning the league the previous season?

8. Despite that collapse the 1955/56 season produced hat-tricks for two Chelsea players whose surnames begin with the same letter. The first came in a 4-4 draw at Fratton Park against Portsmouth on New Year's Eve, while the second came in a 6-1 home win over Everton on 14 April 1956. Who were the two men scoring the hat-tricks?

9. Which Chelsea goalkeeper never missed a league game in the 1957/58 season?

10. Which player burst on to the scene by scoring on the first day of the 1957/58 season, getting two on the first day of the 1958/59 season and finally hitting three on the opening day of the decade's last season in 1959/60?

QUIZ No. 25

CHELSEA IN THE LEAGUE – THE 1960s

1. The significance of Jimmy Greaves to Chelsea's fortunes could not have been more clearly demonstrated by the fact that in his final season before his move to Italy they finished 12th and scored 98 goals, whereas in the following season of 1961/62 they finished bottom, scoring 35 fewer goals. What was the last month they won a game in when they were relegated and which club beginning with the same letter as Chelsea accompanied them on their journey to Division Two?

2. They didn't stay down for long, being promoted as runners-up to Stoke City in 1962/63. Their centre-half and their midfield dynamo played in all 42 league games. Who were they?

3. The battle for promotion went down to the wire, with the crucial match producing a 1-0 away win on 18 May through a Tommy Harmer goal. Without that goal, which was rather fortuitous, their opponents, who missed out on goal average, would have gone up instead of Chelsea. Who were they?

4. Chelsea still had to win convincingly on the last day at home to Portsmouth to ensure their promotion. How did it turn out?

5. From this point on began the most solid years the club had experienced to that point. Only one season in the next seven did they finish outside the top six. Third place was achieved in 1964/65 when which young wing-half demonstrated his arrival on the scene by following up his 41 games the previous season with a full set this time around?

6. Five players took the accolade of leading league goalscorer over the decade, with Bobby Tambling landing it five times. Which two players who share the first letters of their surnames were both top scorers at some point in the decade?

7. 1966/67 was the only season that Chelsea finished outside the top six after their promotion in 1962/63 and they made up for it with a great FA Cup run to the final itself. In what position did they finish that season?

8. In 1968/69 they finished fifth and there were notable hat-tricks by two players. The first was delivered by one of their front men on 19 October 1968 in a 3-0 home win over Leicester City, while the second occurred in a 3-1 win at Ipswich Town on Boxing Day and was extremely rare in that it came from a centre-half. Which two men came up with the hat-tricks?

9. 1969/70 is remembered as a great season because Chelsea broke their duck in the FA Cup but they did tremendously well to finish third in the league after a dreadful start. How many of their first nine games did they win?

10. Two Chelsea players who share the first letter of their surnames were models of consistency throughout that season, with neither of them missing a single game. One was a wing-half and the other a winger. Who were they?

QUIZ No. 26

CHELSEA IN THE LEAGUE – THE 1970s

1. By the mid 1970s Chelsea were in significant decline and it was to be some time in the future before they had sides to compare to the late 1960s and early 1970s. This decade produced two relegations, the first in 1974/75 and the second in 1978/79. One club went down with Chelsea on each of those occasions, one from the north and one from the Midlands. They also share the same colours. Who were they?

2. Like a set of bookends, Chelsea's leading scorer at the decade's start in 1970/71 and their leading scorer at the end in 1979/80 both have surnames that begin with the same letter. The leading scorer in 1975/76 also has a name that begins with that letter. Who are the three players?

3. If Chelsea fans were depressed by the fact that when they were relegated in 1974/75, they won only one of their last 12 games, they needed to brace themselves against the fact that it was worse in 1978/79. Chelsea had one win in the last how many games that season?

4. It wasn't all doom and gloom! The 1976/77 season brought promotion from Division Two when they went up with Wolves. Stamford Bridge was in celebratory mode on the last day of the season when which player scored a hat-trick in a 4-0 win over Hull City?

5. That year's promotion side achieved something that hadn't been done for 66 years. What was it?

6. Who was joint top goalscorer with Peter Osgood in 1972/73?

7. Speaking of which, in that 1972/73 season Peter Osgood wasn't the only player with a name beginning with 'O' to score for Chelsea. Who scored his only Chelsea goal against Stoke City at Stamford Bridge on 7 April 1973?

8.   Those two Chelsea stalwarts Ron Harris and John Hollins were ever-presents in the league twice each over the decade. Who were the only two other players to play every game in a season in that ten-year spell?

9.   It isn't often that you manage to score seven goals on the ground of a team from your own city, but Chelsea did so on 10 November 1979 in a 7-3 win. Who did they beat, and who scored a hat-trick in the game?

10. Of all Chelsea's leading goalscorers over the decade, only Steve Finnieston got over 20 to his name. They came in the promotion season of 1976/77. How many did he score in his 39 games?

QUIZ No. 27

CHELSEA IN THE LEAGUE – THE 1980s

1. This was for the most part a desperate decade in Chelsea's history, although if you are someone who likes to find a silver lining you could say that the club experienced twice as many promotions as relegations. Although they finished 12th in Division Two in 1980/81 there were already signs of future problems concerning runs of bad form. A 1-1 draw at Meadow Lane against Notts County proved to be the last goal scored away all season. In which month did they score it?

2. The season's highlight was a 6-0 win over Newcastle United at Stamford Bridge on 25 October 1980. Which Chelsea player registered a hat-trick in that game?

3. In 1982/83 the club experienced the most terrible season in its history and when the points were added up at the end they had escaped playing in the Third Division by just two. They won just one of the last 11 and it was vital. It came away in Lancashire by 1-0 through a Clive Walker goal in the season's penultimate game. If they had lost it they would have gone down and their opponents would have survived. Who were those opponents?

4. Chelsea were shocked into a response and went from 18th to first the following season, fired by Kerry Dixon's goals, of which there were 28. Who had been the last Chelsea player to score more than that in a league season?

5. Back in the big time Chelsea made themselves at home right away and finished in a commendable sixth spot. An unusual feature that season was the fact that the four games against London rivals Arsenal and Spurs all ended in the same scoreline. What was it?

6. Chelsea's sixth place again in the following season was largely due to a great run in the middle that saw them go undefeated for over three months. However, it was just like them to ruin all their good work by losing their last four games, the last of which was by 5-1 at Stamford Bridge against which club?

7. 1987/88 brought relegation again after one solitary win in their last 26 games. The season's most exciting game was a 4-4 away draw on 19 March 1988 against which club?

8. A tremendous run when they lost once in 33 matches got them promoted again in 1988/89, although they didn't win that season until their seventh game. In their two promotion seasons of 1983/84 and 1988/89 they were accompanied on their upward journey by four clubs. Newcastle United, Sheffield Wednesday and Manchester City constituted three of them while the fourth were which fellow Londoners?

9. Which Chelsea defender was an ever-present in 1981/82 and 1983/84?

10. Back in the top flight again, in 1989/90 Chelsea cemented their fifth-place finish with a 3-1 final-day away win against another London club that were relegated that year. Which club did Chelsea beat and who scored all three of their goals on the day?

QUIZ No. 28

CHELSEA IN THE LEAGUE - THE 1990s

1. The 1990s could be clearly divided in two where Chelsea were concerned as they spent the first half of the decade around mid-table or just below, before cementing a top-six finish or better in the last four years of the century. In fact, in those first six seasons they occupied just two league positions, one of them no fewer than four occasions. What was that position?

2. Three players with a surname beginning with 'S' were top goalscorer or joint-top goalscorer in a season during this decade. Who were they?

3. Derby County and Nottingham Forest don't care for each other overmuch and Chelsea had mixed fortunes when they travelled to the East Midlands in 1990/91. Firstly, on 15 December, they shared a ten-goal thriller with Derby County at the Baseball ground, and then on 20 April they got hammered by Nottingham Forest at the City ground. What were the two scorelines?

4. When Aston Villa came to Stamford Bridge on 15 September 1996, which ex-Blue scored the visitors' goal in a 1-1 draw?

5. Which Chelsea defender scored at both ends when Chelsea lost 3-2 at Derby County on 1 March 1997?

6. Chelsea's attack could be devastating on occasion, and in the 1997/98 season, as well as a 6-2 home win over Crystal Palace, they recorded wins by 6-0 and 6-1 away from home as well. Which two clubs were beaten up on home soil?

7. A particularly memorable match occurred on 12 September 1998 when Chelsea turned a 3-2 deficit into a 4-3 win in the last ten minutes of a pulsating game against Blackburn Rovers at Ewood Park. Who got two late goals that won the game; which Blackburn player who later joined Chelsea scored twice for Rovers; and which Chelsea player with Blackburn connections got a red card?

8. One Manchester United player was particularly kind to Chelsea by scoring for them on two different occasions. The goals came in a 2-2 Old Trafford draw in 1997, and in Chelsea's stunning 5-0 win at Stamford Bridge in 1999. Who was he?

9. Chelsea lost just three times in the league in 1998/99 in finishing third. They were beaten on their travels at Arsenal and Coventry City. Which club ruined what would have been an undefeated home record?

10. When Chelsea lost 1-0 at Anfield against Liverpool on 16 October 1999 they finished the game with nine men on the field. Which two players saw red?

QUIZ No. 29

CHELSEA MANAGERS HAVE THEIR SAY

All these quotes are from Chelsea managers, but not all of them were uttered while in that capacity. Can you identify them in each case?

1. 'This game drives you either to drink or the madhouse; and I'm not going to the madhouse for anybody.'

2. 'When Joe first came to Chelsea he would turn away in disappointment if West Ham had lost. I would smile.'

3. 'How can you tell your wife you are just popping out to play a match and then not come back for five days?' Which manager struggles with the demands of Test cricket?

4. 'The game is about glory. Its about doing things in style, with a flourish, about going out and beating the other lot, not waiting for them to die of boredom.'

5. 'When the sack arrives, I won't cry. I will enjoy my family, then the next month I'll get another club. Remember, the richest managers are those that are sacked the most.'

6. 'It is important to win the games, particularly when the fish are down.' Which manager struggles to get to grips with English expressions?

7. 'General Pinochet tortured a lot of people, but there is no illiteracy in Chile.' Which manager sees the silver lining in a particularly dark cloud?

8. 'Stamford Bridge is fantastic ... for potatoes.' Which manager suggests an alternative use for the property?

9. 'If you're a playboy and you're not there you can't win the FA Cup and be second in the Premier League. That's impossible.' Which manager disagrees with the club's decision to dispense with his services?

10. 'That's ridiculous. He's one of the best central defenders in the world. So be careful what you're saying.' Which manager responding to which Sky pundit's criticism of which player?

QUIZ No. 30

CHELSEA - SEASON 2000/01

1. The traditional curtain-raiser that some managers shamelessly count among the trophies they've won in the game was played at Wembley between Chelsea and Manchester United on 13 August 2000, with Chelsea coming out on top 2-0. Unsurprisingly, Jimmy Floyd Hasselbaink opened the scoring for Chelsea. Who got their second goal?

2. Hasselbaink had quite a season. Not only was he Chelsea's top scorer in the Premier League, but he was also the league's top scorer with how many goals?

3. In what is beginning to sound like the J-FH show, he also found the net four times in a 6-1 win at Stamford Bridge on 21 October 2000 against which Midlands club?

4. On the first day of that October just mentioned Chelsea also won at Stamford Bridge. This time it was against Liverpool and they were helped on their way to a 3-0 win by an own goal after ten minutes from the visiting goalkeeper. Who was he?

5. Which midfielder made the most starts for Chelsea in the league with a total of 35?

6. Two old Chelsea rivals accounted for them in the two domestic cup competitions. They went out in extra time away from home at the first attempt in the League Cup and lost 3-1 away in the FA Cup fifth round. Which two clubs scuppered their progress in these ties?

7. Only one player scored for Chelsea in both those domestic cup competitions. Who was he?

8. In the FA Cup, after beating Peterborough 5-0 at home, they won 4-2 at Gillingham when the 'G' forces were well in evidence. Their four goals were shared equally by two men with a surname starting with that letter. Who were they?

9. Chelsea lost just three times at home all season, and the three clubs that left Stamford Bridge with three points all managed to complete the league double over the Blues. One of them was Leicester City, while the other two had been involved in arguably the greatest play-off final at Wembley three years earlier. Who were the two clubs?

10. Which Sunderland player scored home and away against Chelsea in the Premier League?

QUIZ No. 31

CHELSEA - SEASON 2001/02

1. Chelsea finished in the same league position as they had the previous season. What position was that?

2. Jimmy Floyd Hasselbaink lost the 'golden boot' by one goal to Thierry Henry but a repeat of the goals he scored in 2000/01 was enough to be Chelsea's top scorer by some distance. On both the FA Cup and League Cup fronts though, he had to share the plaudits with which player?

3. Which Chelsea player endeared himself to the fans with a 90th-minute winner at White Hart Lane against Spurs to send his team back west with all three points from a 3-2 win on 16 September 2001?

4. Gianfranco Zola scored three league goals during the season, and his total was matched by another player with a name beginning with 'Z'. Who was he?

5. Which Southampton player, who had scored twice in their home game against Chelsea in the previous season, scored two more at Stamford Bridge this time around as the visitors won 4-2 on New Year's Day?

6. In the return game with Spurs on 13 March 2002, which Chelsea won 4-0, which player scored a hat-trick and which Spurs player got his marching orders?

7. Chelsea reached the FA Cup final before succumbing to Arsenal. On the way they knocked out London clubs in the fourth round and the semi-final. Which two clubs bit the dust?

8. One player got the winning goal in both those rounds, the first of them in the 90th minute of an away replay. Who was he?

9. Which team did Chelsea beat twice in the Premier League and again in the first leg of the League Cup semi-final at Stamford Bridge? The less said about the second leg the better, I'm sure you'll agree!

10. Chelsea had beaten Newcastle United in the quarter-final and had won 2-0 twice away from home to get that far. The two beaten teams played each other in an excellent FA Cup semi-final in 1987. Who were they?

QUIZ No. 32

CHELSEA - SEASON 2002/03

1. The first day of the season started terribly as they went 2-0 down at the home of another London club on 17 August 2002. However, they managed to turn things round with an 84th-minute equaliser before Lampard struck with the winner in the 89th minute. Who were they playing?

2. Chelsea's biggest win of the season came on 22 March 2003 when they beat Manchester City by what score at Stamford Bridge?

3. Which Chelsea player was sent off when they beat Middlesbrough 1-0 in the FA Cup third round at Stamford Bridge on 4 January 2003?

4. Who was Chelsea's top Premier League goalscorer with 14 to his name?

5. Which Chelsea player scored at both ends when Arsenal knocked Chelsea out of the FA Cup 3-1 in a Stamford Bridge quarter-final replay on 25 March 2003?

6. Before going out, Chelsea had beaten two teams on their travels to get that far. They won 4-0 and 2-0 against two clubs beginning with the same letter. Who were they?

7. William Gallas, Frank Lampard and Gianfranco Zola were all on the pitch at some stage of every Premier League game. Which one of the three failed to start just once?

8. Chelsea had to work hard to shake off Gillingham at Stamford Bridge in their first League Cup tie. Who scored both goals in their 2-1 win?

9. Manchester United eventually brought their interest in the competition to an end with a late goal at Old Trafford, but not before they had beaten a fellow Premier League club 4-1 at Stamford Bridge. It was the same score when they met at the same venue in the league the following April. Who were they?

10. The last game of the season was a very tense affair indeed. Chelsea were level on points with their opponents who visited Stamford Bridge needing a draw to cement the last Champions League spot. Chelsea's superior goal difference meant that a win would give them the prize. Chelsea won 2-1. Who did they beat and which visiting player saw red two minutes from the end?

QUIZ No. 33

CHELSEA - SEASON 2003/04

1. Chelsea looked to have a tough start to their Premier League campaign against Liverpool at Anfield on 17 August 2003, but they came away smiling when Hasselbaink's 87th-minute goal gave them a 2-1 win. Which recruit from Manchester United had given the Londoners the lead in the first half?

2. Which club did Chelsea have a great time against in 2003/04, winning by 5-0 away and 5-2 at home, with the help of a Hasselbaink hat-trick on the second occasion?

3. Who was the only Chelsea player to appear in all 38 Premier League matches?

4. Although his goals tally was effectively halved from earlier campaigns, Jimmy Floyd Hasselbaink was still Chelsea's leading goalscorer in the Premier League. But who, with four of the eight goals they scored in the competition, was Chelsea's leading scorer in the FA Cup?

5. In that tournament they had accounted for Watford after a replay in the third round before a 1-0 win in Yorkshire courtesy of a John Terry goal in the next round. Who did they beat?

6. In both the FA Cup and the League Cup Chelsea eventually went out to two clubs whose names begin with the same letter. Who were they?

7. On 21 February 2004 Chelsea made a great start against Arsenal at Stamford Bridge with a first-minute goal. However, things went downhill after that and they eventually lost the game 2-1. The Chelsea player whose afternoon began so promisingly when he scored the early goal ended that afternoon with a red card. Who was he?

8. Appropriately enough, Wayne Bridge scored his first Chelsea goal at the Bridge on 28 December 2003, against the rivals of the club he came from, in a 3-0 home win. Who were they playing?

9.   Which Chelsea player was sent off in the first home game of the season against Leicester City on 23 August 2003 on a day when Chelsea won the football match 2-1 but eventually lost the 'red card' game by the same score when two of the visitors departed in the 84th and 88th minutes?

10. The final game of the season in which Chelsea had finished second in the Premier League saw manager Claudio Ranieri given a Stamford Bridge send off by the home crowd after a 1-0 win over which club?

QUIZ No. 34

CHELSEA - SEASON 2004/05

1. New manager Jose Mourinho delivered the club's first league title for 50 years and broke a few records along the way. One was the Premier League points record and another was the lowest number of goals conceded. What two new records did Chelsea set?

2. Chelsea lost just one league game during the season. It came in October by 1-0 from the penalty spot. Who were they playing, and which player who eventually became a Blue scored the goal?

3. On 23 October 2004 a Gudjohnsen hat-trick contributed largely to a 4-0 home win over Blackburn Rovers. The other goal came from someone who had joined Chelsea from the club they beat. Who was he?

4. Which player had an extremely busy time against Chelsea, and not for the first time in his career? Chelsea won 2-1 at Stamford Bridge on 28 August and he scored at both ends. Then, on 12 February 2005, after changing clubs, he managed to head butt a Chelsea player in the back of his head when Chelsea won away by 1-0, and saw red for his trouble.

5. Chelsea's only ever-present in the Premier League was also their leading scorer in that competition. Who was he?

6. Four Chelsea players made the PFA Team of the Year. They were Petr Čech, John Terry, Frank Lampard and which other player?

7. Which club did Chelsea meet in both domestic cup competitions in 2004/05, beating them 2-0 after extra time away from home in the League Cup, but losing to them 1-0 on the same ground in the FA Cup fifth round?

8. Which two London clubs did Chelsea knock out of the League Cup by 1-0 at home and 2-1 away?

9. Which London ground did John Terry score twice on in a 4-0 Chelsea win on 27 November 2004?

10. Which Chelsea player scored their first goal in the League Cup and their last goal in that same competition when they overcame Liverpool in the final 3-2 to land the trophy?

QUIZ No. 35

CHELSEA - SEASON 2005/06

1. The Premier League title was retained with an unbeaten home record. Only one club took a point away from Stamford Bridge the whole season and they also put Chelsea out of the League Cup on the same ground on penalties. Who were they?

2. Chelsea lost that shoot-out by 5-4. Who was the unlucky man whose penalty didn't find the net?

3. Two new signings got their first Premier League goal for Chelsea against Spurs. The first did so in a 2-0 win at White Hart Lane in August, while the second did so in a 2-1 win at Stamford Bridge in March. Who were the two players?

4. Two players with the same surname scored for Chelsea in their run to the FA Cup semi-final, the goals coming in home games against Huddersfield Town in the third round and Colchester United in the fifth round. Who were the two scorers?

5. In the 3-1 win over Colchester United in that fifth-round tie, who scored the visitors' goal?

6. Who was the only Chelsea player to score in both domestic cup competitions?

7. Chelsea turned in a remarkable performance at Stamford Bridge on 9 April 2006. They found themselves a goal down after ten minutes, and then a man down after 17 minutes when Maniche was sent off. They then went on to win 4-1 with a man short for the rest of the game. Who were they playing?

8. On 15 October 2005 Chelsea came from behind to beat Bolton Wanderers 5-1 at Stamford Bridge. For the visitors a player with a surname beginning with a 'G' was sent off after 58 minutes while the man who gave the visitors a fourth-minute lead also had a name beginning with that letter, his claim to fame being that he could have the longest name of anyone to score against Chelsea. Who were the two men, with a bonus point if you can spell the second correctly?

9. Chelsea had 1-0 home wins on successive weekends in December against two northern clubs, with John Terry scoring the winner on both occasions. Which two teams did Chelsea beat?

10. Who was Chelsea's top scorer in the Premier League with 16 goals to his name?

QUIZ No. 36

CHELSEA - SEASON 2006/07

1. Another magnificent season in which Chelsea finished second in the Premier League, won both domestic cups and were extremely unlucky to go out of the Champions League at the semi-final stage. The Premier League's top goalscorer also played for the club. Who was he?

2. Who scored the first goal for Chelsea in the Community Shield against Liverpool at the Millennium Stadium on 13 August 2006?

3. Which ex-Blue came back to Stamford Bridge to score for Charlton Athletic when they lost 2-1 to Chelsea on 9 September 2006?

4. On the 11th day of the 11th month, Didier Drogba had a great time at Stamford Bridge scoring a hat-trick in Chelsea's 4-0 win over which club?

5. The ups and downs of a footballer's life were well illustrated by what happened to Chelsea's Michael Essien in December 2006. On the tenth of that month he secured Chelsea a 1-1 home draw with a wonder goal six minutes from the end and then on Boxing Day on the same ground he scored an own goal around the same time to allow the visitors to leave with a point from a 2-2 draw. Which two clubs were involved?

6. On 18 April Chelsea won 4-1 away to another London club, with two of their goals coming from a player whose father used to play for the club Chelsea beat. Which player scored those two goals?

7. Which club did Chelsea knock out of both domestic cup competitions?

8. Frank Lampard scored a hat-trick in the FA Cup third round in a 6-1 Chelsea win at Stamford Bridge against which club from the fourth tier of English football?

9. Who scored Chelsea's extra-time winner in the FA Cup semi-final win over Blackburn Rovers at Old Trafford?

10. Which Chelsea player got a red card in the fracas that accompanied the closing stages of their 2-1 win over Arsenal in the League Cup final?

QUIZ No. 37

CHELSEA - SEASON 2007/08

1. Second place again, unbeaten at home again, in two finals, but a very different sort of season due to the club parting company with Jose Mourinho in September and his replacement with Avram Grant. Chelsea's home record was an exact replica of the previous season. What was it?

2. It is unusual for the leading scorer of the team in second place in the league to have just ten goals to his name but that's what happened. He was also Chelsea's top scorer in both cup domestic competitions. Who was he?

3. Chelsea's biggest win in the Premier League came on 27 October 2007 when which northern club were beaten 6-0 at Stamford Bridge?

4. Which club did Chelsea draw 4-4 with in an away game in March 2008?

5. After a 3-1 win over Huddersfield Town in the FA Cup fifth round at Stamford Bridge, Chelsea went out of the competition by 1-0 in the next round against another Yorkshire club. Which one?

6. On the first day of March 2008 Frank Lampard scored from the spot and then got sent off as Chelsea won 4-0 away. Then on 12 March he rattled in four goals in a 6-1 win at Stamford Bridge. Who were Chelsea's two opponents?

7. Spurs finally turned Chelsea over in the League Cup final, but which two clubs from the same city had Chelsea beaten to get there?

8. Which new full-back endeared himself to the home fans when he opened the scoring with a great strike at home to Spurs on 12 January 2008 in a game that Chelsea went on to win 2-0?

9. If you are going to lose 1-0 at Arsenal, as Chelsea did on 16 December 2007, you would rather anyone else scored the goal than this man. Who was he?

10. What was Avram Grant's reward for finishing second, losing the Champions League final on penalties and reaching the League Cup final?

QUIZ No. 38

CHELSEA - SEASON 2008/09

1. After five successive top-two positions in the Premier League, Chelsea had to settle for third place this time around, although they did equal a top-flight record by winning 11 consecutive away games. Which club's record did they equal?

2. They also had the winner of the Premier League's 'golden boot' with 19 goals. Who was he?

3. Scolari's new regime didn't see the season out when he was sacked after a 0-0 home draw with which club on 7 February 2009?

4. Who took over as interim manager, and which job did he continue to carry out alongside the Chelsea managerial position?

5. Which club put Chelsea out of the League Cup on penalties at Stamford Bridge after Chelsea had beaten Portsmouth 4-0 at Fratton Park in the previous round?

6. Chelsea won the FA Cup after beating Everton in the final. Which player scored a hat-trick at Watford in the fifth round, and which other player scored in the quarter-final, semi-final and final?

7. In September 2008 John Terry picked up a red card in a 3-1 away win that was later rescinded. Then in December he got another in a 0-0 away draw that wasn't rescinded. Against which two clubs?

8. Chelsea enjoyed two 5-0 victories a fortnight apart against two northern clubs in the Premier League, the first away from home in October, and the second at Stamford Bridge on the first day of November. Who were the two beaten clubs?

9. Which Chelsea player got the two goals that beat Middlesbrough on 28 January 2009, and then got the winner at West Ham on 25 April as well?

10. Which team were Chelsea trailing to by 1-0 at Stamford Bridge on 17 January 2009 going into the closing stages when Belletti drew them level on 88 minutes before Lampard won it in the 93rd?

QUIZ No. 39

CHELSEA - SEASON 2009/10

1. Chelsea tasted Premier League glory again under their new manager Carlo Ancelotti. Which Italian club did he leave to come to Stamford Bridge?

2. Chelsea lost just one home game in the Premier League. It came on 27 February 2010 when Manchester City won 4-2. They were helped considerably by the fact that Chelsea finished the game with nine men. Which two home players who share the first letter of their surnames saw red?

3. Didier Drogba had a great season, scoring 29 league goals to win the Premier League Golden Boot award. He was also chosen in the PFA Team of the Year along with one other Chelsea player. Who was he?

4. Chelsea's attack came to life in dramatic fashion at Stamford Bridge when 2010 arrived. In just four home games, one in January, one in March, one in April and the last in May, they scored 29 goals. It started against a northern club who were beaten 7-2 on 16 January. Which ex-Chelsea player scored for their opponents that day and who were those opponents?

5. The second club to be hammered were on the wrong end of a 7-1 scoreline and a Frank Lampard four-timer. Which Midlands club was it?

6. In April Chelsea continued on their merry way when Stoke were beaten 7-0 at Stamford Bridge. Who bagged a hat-trick that day?

7. Finally, fed up with scoring a mere seven three times, they went one better in their final game of the season, clinching the league with a Drogba hat-trick and an 8-0 win over which northern club?

8. On 13 March 2010 which ex-Chelsea man scored for West Ham United when Chelsea beat them 4-1 at Stamford Bridge?

9. Chelsea were FA Cup winners again this season after beating Preston North End, Cardiff City, Stoke City, Aston Villa and then Portsmouth in the final itself. Which club had they beaten 5-0 in the third round to set the ball rolling?

10. Salomon Kalou scored in all three of Chelsea's League Cup games. They beat QPR and Bolton Wanderers 1-0 and 4-0 at Stamford Bridge before going out of the competition on penalties after a 3-3 away draw with which club?

QUIZ No. 40

CHELSEA - SEASON 2010/11

1. Second place proved not to be enough to keep Carlo Ancelotti in employment at the season's end, but Chelsea produced the greatest two-match start in the club's history when they won by the same score home and away in those games against two teams that began with the same letter. What was that score and who were those teams?

2. Florent Malouda was Chelsea's top league goalscorer with 13 to his name, and he was also one of three players who were on the field in all 38 matches. The other two shared the first letter of their surname. Who were they?

3. On 2 January 2011 Chelsea's visitors to Stamford Bridge went home with a point from a 3-3 draw but also clocked up a massive seven yellow cards. Who were they?

4. Three days later Chelsea went down 1-0 at Molineux against Wolves. Whose own goal after five minutes proved to be the only score in the match?

5. In the FA Cup Louis Saha scored his usual goal against the Blues and Chelsea went out on penalties after two 1-1 draws with Everton in the fourth round. Which club had Chelsea slaughtered 7-0 in the third round?

6. Which northerners came to Stamford Bridge and won 4-3 in the League Cup in Chelsea's first game of the season in that competition?

7. Which new signing announced his arrival by scoring against both Manchester clubs at Stamford Bridge in the month of March?

8. Fernando Torres scored goals for fun against Chelsea, but when they took the plunge and bought him for a record fee he couldn't seem to remember how he did it, and took 13 games to find the net. His goal finally came in a 3-0 home win on 23 April against which club?

9. Which Chelsea player was dismissed in the 94th minute of the Chelsea v Fulham derby at Stamford Bridge on 10 November 2010, a game that Chelsea won 1-0?

10. Who was the only Chelsea player to be chosen for the PFA Team of the Year?

QUIZ No. 41

CHELSEA - SEASON 2011/12

1. Football is a contradictory business. Chelsea had their worst Premier League season in nine years yet ended up winning the Champions League and the FA Cup. They looked to be going nowhere fast until Andre Villas-Boas was sacked after a 1-0 defeat away to which club on 3 March 2012?

2. What was ironic about the appointment of Roberto Di Matteo as Chelsea manager after that sacking?

3. Which Chelsea player was sent off nine minutes after scoring when Chelsea beat Swansea City 4-1 on 24 September 2011?

4. Which club did Chelsea meet in both the FA Cup and the League Cup during this season?

5. On their way to landing the FA Cup Chelsea won the quarter-final 5-2 and the semi-final 5-1. Which two clubs did they beat?

6. Which Chelsea player scored a hat-trick when they won 5-1 away at Bolton Wanderers in the Premier League on 2 October 2011?

7. A particularly bad tempered derby between QPR and Chelsea at Loftus Road saw the home side prevail 1-0 against a Chelsea side that finished with nine men. Which two of the visitors saw red?

8. Chelsea gained revenge for that defeat in no uncertain terms on 29 April at Stamford Bridge. What score did they beat QPR by and who scored a hat-trick in the game?

9. Chelsea's other local rivals Fulham drew both Premier League games with them 1-1. The scorer of Fulham's goal in both games shared a surname with a player who had left Fulham for Chelsea about 40 years before. What was that surname?

10. A strange one to finish with. Within the space of three days at the end of April and the start of May two opposition players with the same surname scored against Chelsea, the first for QPR and the second for Newcastle United. What was that surname?

QUIZ No. 42

CHELSEA – SEASON 2012/13

1. Chelsea finished third in a season that was notable for yet more managerial musical chairs. Who came in to manage the club after the sacking of Roberto Di Matteo in November?

2. Irony follows Di Matteo around. Which club defeated Chelsea 2-1 in his last league match in charge?

3. Two days before Christmas, Chelsea opened up with both barrels, winning 8-0 at Stamford Bridge. There were seven goalscorers that day. Which club did Chelsea show little festive spirit to, and who was the player who scored twice and then got himself sent off in the return fixture?

4. Before Chelsea disappointed by going out of the competition in the semi-final against Swansea City, the League Cup had produced the season's most exciting game when Manchester United came to the capital on 31 October 2012. What was the score after extra-time?

5. Which club did they blow away 6-0 in their first game in the League Cup on 25 September 2012?

6. Before going out of the FA Cup in the semi-final to Manchester City, Chelsea had accounted for four clubs who all play in red in the shape of Southampton, Brentford, Middlesbrough and Manchester United. In away ties at Southampton and Middlesbrough which Chelsea player managed to part that red sea to score in each game?

7. On 30 January 2013 Reading took a 2-1 lead at home to Chelsea in the 94th minute. Which Chelsea player wiped the smiles from their faces in the 95th minute?

8. Ex-Blues William Gallas and Shaun Wright-Phillips both scored against Chelsea in the Premier League during the season. Which two clubs were they playing for?

9. Petr Čech had the most Premier League starts and Frank Lampard was top league goalscorer with 15, but who was the only Chelsea player to make the PFA Team of the Year?

10. Which player had an absolute nightmare against Chelsea when the visitors won 4-0 at Stoke City on 12 January 2013, scoring two own goals and missing a penalty?

QUIZ No. 43

CHELSEA - SEASON 2013/14

1. There were no trophies to show for the return of the 'Special One' with Chelsea finishing third in the Premier League, although they had a superb record against the sides above them. Jose Mourinho's phenomenal unbeaten home record at Chelsea that stretched back 77 games finally went in April 2014 when which club won 2-1 at Stamford Bridge?

2. The same club knocked Chelsea out of the League Cup as well, but not before Chelsea had won two away games by 2-0 against two clubs that met in the final of the competition in 1969. Who were the two teams?

3. Who, with 14 to his name, was Chelsea's leading Premier League goalscorer?

4. Who scored the first goal of the second coming of the 'Special One' in a 2-0 win over Hull City at Stamford Bridge on 18 August 2013 when he opened the scoring after 13 minutes?

5. Which Sunderland player scored at both ends when Chelsea won there 4-3 in the Premier League on 4 December 2013?

6. Which player who was out on loan at Newcastle United scored for them when they beat Chelsea 2-0 on 2 November 2013 before signing for Chelsea the following season?

7. Chelsea won 3-1 at home to Manchester United in January and 3-1 away to Fulham on the first day of March. Which two Chelsea players registered a hat-trick in those games?

8. Chelsea walloped Arsenal 6-0 at Stamford Bridge on 22 March 2014. Which player who went on to win a Footballer of the Year award scored the sixth goal, and why was the result more sobering than usual for one particular individual?

9. Manchester City knocked Chelsea out of the FA Cup but it didn't stop Chelsea doing them a massive favour in the race for the Premier League title by winning 2-0 at Anfield against Liverpool on 27 April 2014. It was part Mourinho's canniness and part good fortune. The two goals came in the last minute of each half. Which two players scored them?

10. Which player started the most games for Chelsea in the Premier League, with a total of 36 out of a possible 38?

QUIZ No. 44

CHELSEA - SEASON 2014/15

1. Has the 'Special One' still got his mojo? You bet he has! Chelsea sweep to the Premier League title by an eight-point margin and remain unbeaten at Stamford Bridge, with only four clubs managing a draw there. All four games ended in the same score. What was that score and who were the most southerly club to take a point away with them?

2. Which new handful of a centre-forward scored in six of the first seven league games and went on to be the club's top scorer with 20 to his name?

3. The title success was built on a great defence, particularly at Stamford Bridge where the goals against column was in single figures. True or false?

4. Which ex-Chelsea player equalised five minutes from the end against Chelsea on 21 September 2014 while playing for Manchester City?

5. If you didn't know who won the Footballer of the Year award in both its versions you could hazard a guess, but how many Chelsea players were in the PFA Team of the Year?

6. The season's biggest shock came in the FA Cup fourth round at Stamford Bridge when which club from a lower division beat Chelsea 4-2?

7. Chelsea left it late when they grabbed 1-0 wins over Everton at home in the 89th minute, and QPR away in the 88th minute. Which two players got them over the line in each instance?

8. Three men started all 38 Premier League games, with Eden Hazard and John Terry being two of them. The third also got the vital extra-time goal in the League Cup semi-final second leg against Liverpool that took them into a winning final against Spurs. Who was he?

9. The only time that Chelsea scored four goals at home in the league was also the only time they let two in. You know now they won 4-2. Who were they playing?

10. On which ground did Chelsea score six times away from home in the league and what score did they win by on 30 August 2014?

CHELSEA - SEASON 2015/16

1. This wasn't a fall from grace, it was a headlong plunge! The favourites to defend their Premier League title finished tenth, and, after their astonishingly successful home form under Mourinho, actually won fewer home games than two of the relegated clubs whose names began with the same letter. Who were they?

2. The plug was pulled on Jose Mourinho after a 2-1 away defeat on 14 December 2015. Who beat them?

3. The same player who scored the final league goal under Mourinho that night was also the man who scored Chelsea's last League Cup goal of the season when they went out on penalties after a 1-1 draw at Stoke City. Who was he?

4. In the FA Cup Chelsea might have wished they had held on to Lukaku after his two goals for Everton knocked them out of the competition in the quarter-final. Previously they had twice won 5-1 against two teams beginning with 'M'. One of them was MK Dons. Who was the other one?

5. Which player scored on his Chelsea debut in a 3-2 win at West Brom just days after signing for the club?

6. Which Chelsea player got a 98th-minute leveller for them in a 3-3 home draw with Everton after having earlier put through his own net?

7. One Aston Villa player had a torrid time against Chelsea, putting through his own net when they lost 2-0 at Stamford Bridge, and then being sent off at Villa Park when Chelsea won there 4-0. Who was he?

8. In recent times, not too many players have scored hat-tricks against Chelsea, but in this Premier League season it happened twice, against Everton away and Manchester City at home. Which two players accomplished it?

9. There were ominous signs of bad things to come on the opening day of the season at Stamford Bridge on 8 August 2015 with an incident involving Jose Mourinho that ran as long as some West End plays! Who did Chelsea draw 2-2 with that day and which Chelsea player was sent off?

10. Which player, who Chelsea would shortly sign, scored the last goal at Stamford Bridge that season for the visitors, Leicester City, in a 1-1 draw?

QUIZ No. 46

CHELSEA - SEASON 2016/17

1. By October, new manager Antonio Conte had found the key that opened the door to another Premier League title for Chelsea. Their 13 successive wins equalled the most in the top flight and only one club had previously recorded more than 93 points. Who were they?

2. They went out of the League Cup to a London club in the shape of West Ham United, and played two more London clubs, namely Spurs and Arsenal, in the semi-final and final of the FA Cup. Which other London club did they beat 4-0 in the FA Cup fourth round at Stamford Bridge?

3. Who was the only Chelsea player to score in both those domestic cup competitions?

4. Which defender was the only man to start all 38 league games, and which man weighed in with 20 Premier League goals to be top scorer for the club?

5. The season's most significant game was the 3-1 win at Manchester City on 3 December 2016 when Chelsea went behind to an own goal just before half-time, only to turn things round spectacularly in the second half. Which two Manchester City players contrived to get themselves sent off in added-on time?

6. When Chelsea beat Southampton 4-2 at Stamford Bridge on 25 April 2017 both the visitors' goals came from ex-Chelsea players. Who were they?

7. Which player left Chelsea for £52 million during the season to sample the dubious delights of the Chinese Super League?

8. Chelsea met Watford in the second and the second-from-last game of the season, beating them 2-1 at their place and 4-3 at the Bridge. Which Watford player found the net in both games?

9. Before their eventual League Cup exit, Chelsea had been involved in a tight tussle at Leicester that ended in a 2-2 stalemate after 90 minutes. Which Chelsea player decided the tie with two goals in three minutes in the opening moments of extra time?

10. Which player scored a late consolation goal for Arsenal when they lost 3-1 at Stamford Bridge on 4 February 2017 before later joining Chelsea?

QUIZ No. 47

CHELSEA - SEASON 2017/18

1. There were too many tensions at the club for a serious defence of the Premier League title and Chelsea eventually finished a massive 30 points off the pace in which position?

2. Two men with surnames beginning with 'A' were prominent during the season, with one of them missing just one league game and the other being selected for the PFA Team of the Year. Who were the two players?

3. Who scored a hat-trick when Chelsea won 4-0 at Stoke City on 23 September 2017?

4. Chelsea enjoyed playing Stoke and saw the old year out on 30 December 2017 by beating them 5-0, this time at Stamford Bridge. Which player with a surname starting with a 'Z' got Chelsea's final goal of 2017 in the 88th minute of that game?

5. In the new year Chelsea lost to Bournemouth and beat Crystal Palace, both times at Stamford Bridge. In each game an ex-Chelsea player scored against his old club. Who were the two men?

6. Michy Batshuayi scored a hat-trick in Chelsea's first League Cup tie at the Bridge when they beat which Midlands club 5-1?

7. Chelsea's interest in that competition was ended in the two-leg semi-final against Arsenal. Which Chelsea player was unfortunate to score an own goal in the second leg at the Emirates?

8. The high point of the season was winning the FA Cup at Wembley against Manchester United. They had started out needing penalties to get past the third round after bringing Norwich City back to London for a replay. They did it the hard way by having two players sent off in extra time. Who were they?

9. Norwich City were in the division below Chelsea, and in winning the trophy Chelsea experienced victory over one other club from a lower division on their march to Wembley. It came in a 4-0 home win in the fifth round. Who did they beat?

10. On 17 September 2017 Chelsea drew 0-0 at home with another London club and one of Chelsea's defenders was sent off. Within two years he was playing for the team he was sent off against. Who did Chelsea play that day and which player got an early bath?

QUIZ No. 48

CHELSEA - SEASON 2018/19

1. Chelsea ended the season in third spot after a few ups and downs and were beaten just once at home in the Premier League all season. Who beat them?

2. Which player scored Chelsea's last goal when they won 3-0 at Huddersfield on the opening day, and their first goal the following week in a 3-2 win over Arsenal?

3. Chelsea drew 1-1 at home to Liverpool and 1-1 away to Manchester United. In both those games ex-Blues got the goals that stopped Chelsea winning. Who were the two men?

4. On 10 February 2019 Chelsea suffered their worst defeat for 28 years. Which club inflicted it and by what score?

5. Not for the first time, which player was Chelsea's 'Mr Reliable', appearing in every Premier League game?

6. Who scored his first Premier League goal for Chelsea in a 3-0 win at Southampton on 7 October 2018?

7. Which experienced front man scored twice in a 5-0 win over Huddersfield Town on 2 February 2019 after joining Chelsea in the January transfer window?

8. Manchester clubs knocked Chelsea out of both domestic cup competitions. True or false?

9. After a fine win in their first League Cup tie away to Liverpool, Chelsea were given a real helping hand at Stamford Bridge when they won 3-2 with the assistance of two own goals. Who were their generous opponents and what was strange about one of the own goals?

10. Winning the Europa League didn't save Maurizio Sarri's job, but for me the season's greatest moment came at Stamford Bridge on 8 April 2019 and showed what a massive loss to the club Eden Hazard's move to Spain would be. He scored a breathtaking goal that night that you could not see without leaping into the air with the sheer joy of it. Which club conceded it in a game in which he scored the other goal as well in Chelsea's 2-0 win?.

QUIZ No. 49

CHELSEA - SEASON 2019/20

1. Frank Lampard was given a shot at the manager's job and finished a respectable fourth in the oddest season of league football in the game's history due to the pandemic. Which player, who spent more time on the pitch in the Premier League than anyone else, scored his first league goal for the club in a 1-1 draw with Leicester City in Stamford Bridge's first match of the season?

2. On 14 September Chelsea went to Molineux and beat Wolves 5-2. Which player found the net four times, three for Chelsea and one for Wolves?

3. In the League Cup which club did Chelsea trounce 7-1 before the disappointment of going out at home to Manchester United?

4. There was a very rare occurrence in the FA Cup in a season in which Chelsea reached the final. Chelsea met the same club in the same round on the same ground with the same scoreline in 2019/20 as they had in 2018/2019. It was the third round at Stamford Bridge and the score was 2-0 to Chelsea. Who did they play?

5. On 26 October which Chelsea player scored his first Premier League goals for the club when his hat-trick enabled them to win 4-2 at Burnley?

6. Which Manchester United player's own goal in the FA Cup semi-final against Chelsea helped cement the Blues' 3-1 win?

7. Which Chelsea defender got both Chelsea goals in a 2-2 draw at Leicester on the first day of February 2020?

8. Which two players who were no stranger to the odd red card got sent off against Chelsea during the season, one of them while playing at Stamford Bridge for Manchester City and the other while performing a probably unique double by getting sent off for Arsenal against Chelsea when in a previous existence he had done the exact opposite?

9. Chelsea lost out 2-1 to Arsenal in the FA Cup final but created a new club record in having the oldest and youngest to play for the club in an FA Cup final. Who were the two players?

10. The referee for the showpiece game would not be popular if spotted in the Fulham Road because he sent off Chelsea's Mateo Kovacic. Who was he and what earlier offence might also be taken into consideration?

CHELSEA - SEASON 2020/21

1. I wasn't overpleased about Frank Lampard's sacking but you couldn't argue with that Champions League trophy that made its way to Stamford Bridge at the season's end. After he took over, Thomas Tuchel went 13 games in all competitions without defeat, breaking which Chelsea manager's previous club record from the start of his tenure?

2. When that run ended on 3 April 2021 in somewhat crazy circumstances against West Bromwich Albion at Stamford Bridge, which Chelsea player was sent off and how many goals did the two Premier League meetings with the Albion produce?

3. It was another Albion that Chelsea had begun the season against when they travelled to Brighton on 14 September, ending up with a 3-1 win. Their first two scorers in the Premier League in 2020/21 began with the same letter. Who were they?

4. On 31 October 2020 Chelsea beat Burnley 3-0 at Turf Moor, and on the same day of the month in January they won the return 2-0 at Stamford Bridge. In the first game Chelsea had two scorers with surnames beginning with the last letter of the alphabet, and in the second game their two goals were scored by players whose surnames begin with the first letter of the alphabet. Who were the four players involved?

5. Which Yorkshire club did Chelsea knock out of both domestic cup competitions, by 6-0 in the League Cup at home and by 1-0 away in the FA Cup?

6. The two clubs that eventually put paid to Chelsea's hopes of winning those competitions had met each other previously in the finals of both the FA Cup and the League Cup. Who were those two clubs?

7. Who scored a hat-trick when Chelsea beat Luton Town 3-1 in the FA Cup fourth round at Stamford Bridge?

8. Who was the only other player to register a hat-trick in a domestic cup competition, his coming in the League Cup?

9. Chelsea's top scorer in the Premier League had just seven goals to his name. Who was he and what was unusual about his achievement?

10. Which club did Mason Mount score against from the penalty spot in a 1-1 away draw on 20 February 2021?

QUIZ No. 51

CRYPTIC CHELSEA - PART 1

Can you identify the Chelsea players below? You are given the dates they played for Chelsea, the number of league appearances they made and a cryptic clue.

1. Great jazz trumpet player – 362 league games – 1946–57

2. Often used off the tee, except on a par three – 44 league games – 1980–83

3. Virginian home of the CIA – 142 league games – 1975–80

4. Best to take one of these with you if it looks like rain – 8 league games – 1971–74

5. Musical and Scottish football club – 5 league games – 1968

6. British prime minister from the inter-war period – 187 league games – 1966–74

7. Landlady at 221B Baker Street – 145 league games – 1968–74 and 1983/84

8. Jelly makers 133 league games – 1978–83

9. More than one Church of England parish priest – 158 league games – 1950–56

10. Sounds like what you want a winger to be – 162 league games – 1982–87

QUIZ No. 52

CRYPTIC CHELSEA - PART 2

Can you identify the Chelsea players below? You are given the dates they played for Chelsea, the number of league appearances they made and a cryptic clue.

1. People do this a lot about football – 118 league games – 1933–47

2. Hollywood's master of suspense – 96 league games – 1988–2001

3. Old-fashioned copper from Dock Green – 335 league games – 1983–92

4. Two presidents of the United States own this surname – 61 league games – 1957–62

5. Free shot after a mishit in a friendly game of golf, if there is such a thing! – 58 league games – 1969–72

6. 19th-century French novelist – 229 league games – 1996–2003

7. Great American boxing champion – 175 league games – 1969–78

8. Danger in garden – 245 league games – 2012–19

9. Upmarket car – 324 league games – 1948–56

10. There are a few of these in Madison County – 176 league games – 1958–66

QUIZ No. 53

CRYPTIC CHELSEA - PART 3

Can you identify the Chelsea players below? You are given the dates they played for Chelsea, the number of league appearances they made and a cryptic clue.

1. Annual US film award – 131 league games – 2012–17

2. Famous 19th-century novelist – 48 league games – 1989–93

3. Opposite of foolish – 332 league games – 1990–2001

4. Nice motorbike! – 30 league games – 1997–2001

5. Biblical figure – 87 league games – 2012–20

6. Defective, not working – 81 league games – 2003–06

7. Capital city – 51 league games – 1984–87

8. Small bird – 69 league games – 1974–81

9. Actor who played TV's 'Maverick' – 105 league games – 1972–78

10. The fort that Goldfinger broke into – 20 league games – 1962–65

QUIZ No. 54

CRYPTIC CHELSEA - PART 4

Can you identify the Chelsea players below? You are given the dates they played for Chelsea, the number of league appearances they made and a cryptic clue.

1. Expert with a knife and the club's 'star man' into the bargain – 76 league games – 1944–51

2   *Pickwick Papers* character – 38 league games – 1970/71

3. Man the apple fell on – 165 league games – 1990–99

4. Midlands forest – 16 league games – 1971–76

5. Town famous for its bookshops – 108 league games – 1974–79

6. Sounds small, but he wasn't – 55 league games – 2001–04

7. City in Texas – 9 league games – 1967–72

8. Young male suitor who won Ascot's King George two years running in the 1990s – 119 league games – 1973–78

9. Candles have them (two players for the price of one here) – 71 league games – 1954–56 and 152 league games – 1974–79 and 1986–88

10. Two men who met up in Africa in 1871
    20 league games – 1955–59
    109 league games – 1971–79

QUIZ No. 55

CRYPTIC CHELSEA - PART 5

Can you identify the Chelsea players below? You are given the dates they played for Chelsea, the number of league appearances they made and a cryptic clue.

1. There are 12 of these in the Derby at Epsom – 65 league games – 1994–96

2. Good advice if you are dehydrated – 12 league games – 2017–2022

3. Pink Floyd guitarist – 8 league games – 2019–still at club

4. Isaac's dad and Lot's uncle – 56 league games – 2016–2021

5. Add one letter to the middle of his name and he's in The Who – 110 league games – 1990–93

6. The most northerly of England's two famous public schools – 304 league games – 1911–26

7. First word of sadly demised London football ground – 74 league games – 1961–65

8. Became King of Scotland in 1057 after the death of Macbeth – 27 league games – 1961/62

9. A great cricketer, an area of Los Angeles and a league title winner with Ipswich Town – 12 league games – 1955–60

10. Coming together of a London football ground and a part of the body – 54 league games – 2014–still at the club

CUP CAPTAINS

1. Who, in the 1915 FA Cup final against Sheffield United, became the first man to lead Chelsea out in a major final?

2. Who, in 1965, became the first man to lead Chelsea to victory in a League Cup final?

3. Who was the first man to hold the FA Cup aloft for Chelsea?

4. Who was the first man to captain Chelsea to win both domestic trophies?

5. Up to and including the 2020/21 season, who has captained Chelsea in a final the most times?

6. Who is the only man to captain Chelsea to two European trophies?

7. Which Chelsea captain has led Chelsea to a European trophy win against the same club he has captained Chelsea against in a losing FA Cup final?

8. Who is the only Chelsea captain to lose an FA Cup final in one season and come back to win it the next?

9. Who was their captain when Chelsea lost the 2002 FA Cup final to Arsenal?

10. No Chelsea captain has led them to win a major trophy in more than one century. True or false?

QUIZ No. 57

'DON'T QUOTE ME ON THAT'

1. 'If promotion with Swindon and keeping Chelsea in 11th place qualifies a man to lead England in a campaign against the Germans, Argentinians and the French, a bloke who can make a paper aeroplane is qualified to pilot a jumbo jet.' Which manager fails to see the attraction of which other manager?

2. 'He's like a Yorkshireman with a Portuguese accent.' Which manager about which other manager?

3. 'He always had to be one up on you. If you told him you'd been to Tenerife, he'd say he'd been to Elevenerife.' Which Chelsea player about which Chelsea figure?

4. 'We will not miss him. He can't head the ball and he rarely passes the ball more than three metres.' The president of which club airs his feelings about which player joining Chelsea?

5. 'I thought Christians were supposed to forgive people for their sins but that doesn't seem to be the case with me.' Which two men with Chelsea connections are involved in this argument over selection for the national side?

6. 'The moment I turned up for training and saw him I knew it was time to go.' Which Chelsea player about which other Chelsea player in 1997?

7. 'My pot-bellied pigs don't squeal as much as him.' Which player with Chelsea connections after being sent off for a foul on which Chelsea player?

8. 'You wouldn't trust a learner driver with a Formula One car.' Which England manager on whose elevation to the job of managing Chelsea?

9. 'When he's prepared to put money into the club, or even pay for his own tickets, then he will be entitled to his opinion.' Which Chelsea part-owner about which politician and talk-show host?

10. 'I am deeply sorry for my inexcusable behaviour. I apologise also to my manager, playing colleagues and everyone at Liverpool Football Club for letting them down.' Which player about which incident involving which Chelsea player?

QUIZ No. 58

FANS

1. Which actress and Chelsea fan sounds like a small motorist?

2. Two Chelsea fans supported other clubs in TV roles; one went to Craven Cottage in *The Sweeney*, while the other supported Newcastle United in *The Likely Lads*. Who were the two actors?

3. Which superb opening batsman who played Test cricket for England is a Chelsea fan?

4. Which British prime minister and president of the United States who were in power at the same time were both Chelsea fans?

5. Perhaps it was written in the stars that this man would be a Chelsea fan! Who is he?

6. This Chelsea fan can turn the making of a cake into an erotic experience. Who is she?

7. These two actors are linked by the fact that they both ended up in Brighton, the first in *Brighton Rock* and the second in *Quadrophenia*. The other thing that links them is that they are both Chelsea fans. Who are they?

8. Which comedian and Chelsea fan shares a surname with a Chelsea full-back who played for the club between 1971 and 1983?

9. Which English actor who shares his surname with a great fast bowler from the 1950s and 1960s is a Chelsea fan?

10. The way he zips around that snooker table at 100 miles an hour makes you think that this Chelsea fan might be a useful winger. Who is he?

THE ULTIMATE CHELSEA QUIZ BOOK

QUIZ No. 59

FOOTBALLER OF THE YEAR

The two main Footballer of the Year awards are the Football Writers' Association Award and the Professional Footballers' Award. The first of them started in 1948 while the latter began in 1974.

1. Gianfranco Zola was the only Chelsea player to win the FWA Footballer of the Year award in the 20th century. Four players with a four-letter surname had done so before him. They played for Luton Town, Manchester United, Manchester City and Liverpool and were successful in 1959, 1968, 1969 and 1984. Who were the four players?

2. Which two Chelsea players in recent times have won both awards?

3. Which player who went on to win the FWA award with another club in 2011 claimed the Young Player of the Year award while with Chelsea in 2004?

4. Besides the answer to question two, who is the only other Chelsea player to land the PFA award, which he did in 2005?

5. In that same year of 2005, which Chelsea player took the FWA award?

6. Who is the only Chelsea player to win the Young Player of the Year award and both the senior awards?

7. Which player won both the main awards with Spurs in 1987 and then made 16 appearances for Chelsea in 1991?

8. The only man to win the FWA award in both the 1950s and 1960s later became Chelsea's manager. Who was he?

9. Jose Mourinho won the media and sponsor's Manager of the Year award three times. Who is the only other Chelsea manager to win it?

10. Which two players won the European Footballer of the Year award with the same Italian club, one in this century and the other in the 1980s, and also played for Chelsea in their careers?

QUIZ No. 60

FULHAM ROAD FAVOURITES No. 1 – ROY BENTLEY

1. Roy Bentley captained the first Chelsea side to win the league title in 1955 and was a talismanic figure. As a youngster he was on the books of both teams in his home city but played league football for neither of them. In which city was he born?

2. His breakthrough came in a Newcastle United team full of goals just after the war. Chelsea got something of a bargain in January 1948 when they handed over what sum for his services?

3. One number figures twice in his Chelsea records. In 1952/53 he scored in this number of consecutive league games, while this was also the number of seasons he was top or joint-top league goalscorer for Chelsea. What is that number?

4. In the mid-1950s he scored Stamford Bridge hat-tricks in wins by 4-3 and 6-1 against a team from the North East and another from Merseyside. Who were the two clubs?

5. He received 12 England caps and scored nine goals for his country, including a Wembley hat-trick in a 3-2 win over which nation on 10 November 1954?

6. His first and last games for Chelsea were both at Stamford Bridge and both against opposition from Yorkshire. Which two clubs did they play?

7. When his first league goal for Chelsea arrived, it wasn't at Stamford Bridge but came in a 2-0 win on another London ground. Which one?

8. When he signed off after 366 appearances in all competitions for Chelsea, he joined two other London clubs, playing with distinction for them 188 times in the league, mostly as a centre-half. Which two clubs did he play for?

9. His Chelsea career had ended on 19 September 1956, but on 28 April 1956 in the previous season he scored his last Chelsea goals when he bagged both of them in a 2-1 win at Stamford Bridge against which Lancastrian club?

10. Roy went into management when his career ended, firstly at Reading between 1963 and 1969 and then at another club from 1969 to 1972. This club were known by one name when he started and another name by the time he left. Who were they?

QUIZ No. 61

FULHAM ROAD FAVOURITES No. 2 – PETER BONETTI

1. I saw a lot of Peter Bonetti's performances in Chelsea's goal in the 1960s and I have never before or since seen a goalkeeper who could pluck a cross from the air like he could. Nowadays, of course, it's rare to see a goalkeeper catch a ball, and when he does he pitches forward on to the ground inviting the world to applaud him and waste a little time! It's easy to remember how many league games Peter played for Chelsea. Can you?

2. This graceful ability to fly through the air got the Chelsea goalkeeper a nickname. What was it?

3. His Chelsea debut came on 2 April 1960 in a 3-0 win over which northern club at Stamford Bridge?

4. Which Scandinavian country provided the opposition when he was awarded his first England cap in a 2-0 away win on 3 July 1966?

5. He played seven times for his country, and that figure would have been considerably higher but for the consistency of Gordon Banks. He has been unfairly blamed down the years for England's collapse against West Germany in 1970, but how many goals did he concede in his six previous England performances?

6. The months between May and October 1975 were interesting ones in the life of Peter Bonetti. Chelsea dispensed with his services in May and then changed their minds in October. In the gap Peter played in the North American League with which club?

7. Chelsea's change of heart allowed Peter Bonetti to play for the club for more seasons than anyone else. How many?

8. His final game for the club came against London rivals in a 1-1 draw at Stamford Bridge in the penultimate game of the 1978/79 season on 14 May 1979. Who were the London rivals?

9. Upon leaving Chelsea, which Scottish club did he play for later in 1979 before finally retiring in 1980?

10. Did he play more or less than 100 games for Chelsea in the two domestic cup competitions?

QUIZ No. 62

FULHAM ROAD FAVOURITES No. 3 – DIDIER DROGBA

1. The perfect player for the big occasion, front man Didier Drogba never gave defences a moments rest. He came to Chelsea's attention with two goals and a superb display for Marseille in the second leg of the 2003/04 UEFA Cup semi-final when they knocked out which English club?

2. He came to Stamford Bridge in July 2004 when they paid out a club record to land him. How much?

3. He had two spells at Chelsea and spent the bulk of his career there. However, he did play club football in five other countries besides England. Which five?

4. During his career he won a couple of African Footballer of the Year awards. Which African country did he play for and captain?

5. He scored his first Chelsea goal in a 2-0 away win in the Premier League at another London club on 24 August 2004. Who did Chelsea beat that day?

6. In the following month he scored his first goals in Europe for the Blues when he netted two of the three in their first match Champions League away win against which club?

7. In 2006/07 Didier Drogba became the first player to score 30 goals in a season for Chelsea in all competitions since which man in 1984/85?

8. On 10 March 2012 Didier Drogba became the first African player to score 100 Premier League goals when he grabbed Chelsea's winner at Stamford Bridge against which club?

9. Drogba played his last game for Chelsea on the final day of the 2014/15 season, but scored his last goal for the club nearly a month earlier. Chelsea won both games 3-1, his final game coming at home and his final goal away. Which two teams did they play?

10. Drogba's goalscoring record in domestic cup finals is phenomenal and will probably never be approached. In the 2015 League Cup final he was on the pitch for just the last moments of the game so we can rule that one out, but he otherwise played in four FA Cup finals, scoring in all of them, and three League Cup finals likewise. Chelsea won all but one of those games and Drogba's goals beat one club in both competitions. Who were the only club Chelsea lost to when he scored in a final and which club did they beat in both the FA Cup final and the League Cup final?

QUIZ No. 63

FULHAM ROAD FAVOURITES No. 4 – HUGHIE GALLACHER

1. He stood just 5ft 5ins off the ground but he was dynamite on a football field, scoring a career total of 463 goals despite the brutal treatment he received from opponents. Starting out with his beloved Queen of the South outside league football, he eventually joined another Scottish club, his phenomenal goalscoring helping them to their only Scottish Cup win in 1924. Who were they?

2. Coming south to England he captained which club to the league title in 1926/27, scoring 36 times in 38 games in the process?

3. After 143 goals for that club in 174 games in all competitions he came much further south to Chelsea against the wishes of the fans of his earlier club. What fee did Chelsea pay to secure his services in 1930?

4. His second game for Chelsea was back at the ground he came from and set a new record crowd of 68,386 for the stadium that still stands today. In his first home match for Chelsea three days later, on 6 September 1930, he scored his first goals for the club when they beat which northern club 6-2?

5. He was a member of the 'Wembley Wizards' Scotland team that beat England 5-1 in 1928 and was a regular scorer for his country. He played in 20 internationals. How many goals did he score?

6. He scored 72 goals in 132 league games for Chelsea, with hat-tricks coming against two clubs that met each other in the 1955 FA Cup final. Who were they?

7. His goal in a fourth-round FA Cup tie that helped Chelsea win 3-1 at Stamford Bridge on 23 January 1932 was his only FA Cup goal against a London club. Which one was it?

8. He scored in his last game for Chelsea on 3 November 1934 when they lost 5-2 in Yorkshire against which club?

9. He moved to which club in November 1934 for £2,750, helping them reach second place in the league in 1935/36 with his prolific scoring?

10. During his career he played for three clubs who play in black and white stripes. Who were they?

QUIZ No. 64

FULHAM ROAD FAVOURITES No. 5 – JIMMY GREAVES

1. Football's greatest goalscorer arrived on the scene as a 17-year-old and like every other debut in his career, he found the net in his first one in a 1-1 away draw on which London ground?

2. They played football on Christmas Day in 1957 and 27,036 fans were royally entertained at Stamford Bridge when Chelsea won 7-4 with Jimmy Greaves hitting four of them. Incidentally, the team Chelsea beat that day levelled things up on Boxing Day by winning the return 3-0. Who were they?

3. He topped Chelsea's goalscoring charts in each of the four seasons he lit up Stamford Bridge, and scored 124 times in 157 league matches. What did he do in his final season of 1960/61 that no other Chelsea leading scorer has done?

4. On which Yorkshire ground did Jimmy Greaves score his first away hat-trick in a 3-2 win on 15 February 1958?

5. In the 1959/60 season Chelsea had two exciting encounters in the league with the same club, drawing 4-4 at home and winning 5-4 away. Jimmy Greaves got all five away goals and three of the four at home. Who were Chelsea playing?

6. There were two other occasions when he scored five in a game. They came in a 6-2 home win on 30 August 1958 and in a 7-1 home win on 3 December 1959. The two defeated clubs were Midlands neighbours. Who were they?

7. The northern club that he scored four times against in a 6-1 away win for Chelsea on 25 March 1960 were also the club he scored his first FA Cup goal against on 3 January 1959 when Chelsea again won away, this time by 4-1. Which club were they?

THE ULTIMATE CHELSEA QUIZ BOOK

Who did England play when Jimmy Greaves scored on his debut for his country when they went down 4-1 away in May 1959? Three years later he went back and scored a hat-trick for England on the same ground and this time they won.

9. Cup goals weren't his strong point during his time at Chelsea. In the FA Cup his last goal for Chelsea was against a Yorkshire club that no longer plays league football, and in the League Cup he scored twice in Chelsea's first-ever game in the competition in a 7-1 away win against another London club. Which two clubs are involved here?

10. After 29 April 1961 some of the joy went out of Stamford Bridge after he signed off with all four goals in a 4-3 win before leaving for Italy. Who did they beat and which Italian club did he join?

QUIZ No. 65

FULHAM ROAD FAVOURITES No. 6 – RON HARRIS

1. For nearly 20 years Ron Harris was a terrier in the tackle for Chelsea, breaking up attacks and giving it short and accurate to the playmakers. Solid as a rock. What was his endearing nickname?

2. Although the result wasn't what was hoped for, what was significant about Ron's captaining Chelsea in the 1967 FA Cup final against Spurs at Wembley?

3. His debut for Chelsea at Stamford Bridge on 24 February 1962, in a match Chelsea won 1-0, was against the same Yorkshire club he scored his first Chelsea goal against in a 3-2 away defeat in the same month two years later. Who were they?

4. When you add up all his games for Chelsea he comfortably heads the field. If you put his league appearances, domestic cup appearances, and European games together they come to just six short of which round figure?

5. For someone whose job was tackling, he didn't miss many games over the years. How many seasons did he play all 42 league matches?

6. On 30 August 1972 Chelsea drew 0-0 at Old Trafford. During the game George Best came through a group of players with a vindictive tackle that broke Alan Hudson's right ankle. When Alan asked George in colourful language why he had done it – in a nightclub, naturally – what was George's reply?

7. Ron Harris scored 13 goals in his league career. Who were the only two London clubs that he scored against?

8. Ron scored his final Chelsea goal in March 1980, and played his last game for the club on 3 May of the same year, both games taking place at Stamford Bridge with Chelsea winning 2-1 and 3-0 against two Second Division clubs from Lancashire. Who were they?

9. After Chelsea, Ron Harris played 60 league games for another London club between 1980 and 1983. Which one?

10. He had a fleeting managerial career for six months in 1984 with which southern club?

QUIZ No. 66

FULHAM ROAD FAVOURITES No. 7 – EDEN HAZARD

1. Arguably the most gifted player to appear for Chelsea, you found yourself watching him rather than the play. On occasion he could take the game to a higher level altogether. Which club did Chelsea buy him from in June 2012 for £32 million?

2. In August 2012 he made his league debut for Chelsea at a place with links to George Orwell, and then, three days later, he made his Stamford Bridge debut against a place associated with Oscar Wilde. Which two clubs did Chelsea play?

3. His first Premier League goal for Chelsea came in a 2-0 home win on 25 August 2012, while his first Premier League hat-trick came on the same ground in a 3-0 win on 8 February 2014. Both games were against the same club. Which one?

4. How many times in his seven seasons at the club was he Chelsea's leading league goalscorer?

5. Winning over 100 caps for Belgium, he captained them to their best-ever World Cup position in the 2018 tournament. Which country did he score his final goal against in that competition?

6. On 3 May 2015 Hazard's goal in a 1-0 win at Stamford Bridge clinched the Premier League title. It came when his penalty was saved and he headed in the rebound. Who were Chelsea playing?

7. Which club did Eden Hazard score a hat-trick against when Chelsea won 4-1 at Stamford Bridge on 15 September 2018?

8. On Boxing Day of that same year in a 2-1 away win he scored his 100th Chelsea goal. Who did they beat?

9. On 4 February 2017, in a 3-1 win at Stamford Bridge, he scored a wonderful goal after a run from the halfway line that left three defenders in his wake, one of them not realising how deceptively strong he was as he literally bounced off him. Who did Chelsea beat that day?

10. In which country did Eden Hazard score his final goal for Chelsea?

QUIZ No. 67

FULHAM ROAD FAVOURITES No. 8 – FRANK LAMPARD

1. A superb midfielder with an uncanny ability to be in the right place to score, as his record as leading goalscorer in Chelsea's history proves beyond doubt. He also found the net 29 times for England. Only three other post-war midfielders have got more than 20 goals for England without scoring as many as Frank. Who are they?

2. In what year did Frank Lampard make the move across the capital from east to west by joining Chelsea from West Ham United, and how much did Chelsea pay for him?

3. Against which club did he make his Chelsea league debut in a 1-1 draw at Stamford Bridge?

4. Frank ended up with 106 England caps. Which other England player ended up with exactly the same number?
   A) Bobby Charlton B) Ashley Cole C) Bobby Moore
   D) Billy Wright

5. Frank Lampard is in the top-ten post-war England goalscorers, a great feat for a midfielder. Two players with surnames beginning with 'L' are in front of him on the list, one by a single goal and the other by 19. Who are they?

6. It would have given him great pleasure to score his 200th Chelsea goal on 17 March 2013 against West Ham United, but earlier, on 20 December 2009, he had scored Chelsea's goal against the same club from the penalty spot in a 1-1 draw at Stamford Bridge. What was unusual about it?

7. In early May 2013 Frank Lampard scored both Chelsea's goals in a 2-1 away win. The first of them equalled the Chelsea goalscoring record and the second broke it. Whose record did he break, and against which club?

8. On 25 February 2012 at Stamford Bridge, Frank Lampard became the only man to score at least ten goals in nine consecutive Premier League seasons when he scored that afternoon in a 3-0 win. Earlier, in April 2005, his two goals away from home had clinched Chelsea's first title for 50 years. Both games were against the same club. Which one?

9. Which three 'City's' has Frank played for in his club career?

10. It was a shame Frank wasn't given more time as Chelsea's manager. He led the team out when they lost in the 2020 FA Cup final to Arsenal. Which five men have also had the experience of managing Chelsea in a losing FA Cup final, this phenomenon happening in 1915, 1967, 1994, 2002 and 2017?

QUIZ No. 68

FULHAM ROAD FAVOURITES No. 9 – PETER OSGOOD

1. When Peter Osgood burst on to the scene like a meteor in the mid-1960s, it didn't take long before a new chant could be heard on the terraces at Stamford Bridge. What was it?

2. He scored 105 goals in 289 league games for the Blues, but how many times was he Chelsea's top scorer in a season?

3. He was turning in one brilliant display after another when it all came to an end in a League Cup tie at Blackpool on 5 October 1966 when he sustained a broken leg in a challenge with a young player who would eventually captain a side to win the European Cup. Who was he?

4. He played in all 42 league games just once for Chelsea. In which season did it occur?

5. Players like Marsh, Bowles, Hudson and Osgood and a few more we could mention didn't get too many chances in an England shirt at that time and he really should have got more than the four caps he received against Belgium, Romania, Czechoslovakia and his only cap at Wembley against which country?

6. Peter Osgood scored goals for Chelsea in the league, the FA Cup, the League Cup, the Fairs Cup and the European Cup Winners' Cup. In which of these five competitions did he average more than a goal a game?

7. One London club got slaughtered on their own ground four times by Peter Osgood. In December 1969 he scored four goals when Chelsea won 5-1 in the league. Then he scored when they won there in the FA Cup fifth round by 4-1 the following February. In the next season he scored there again in a 2-2 draw in the FA Cup third round and then, in November of 1971, did so yet again in a 3-2 league win. Who were the London club that were sick of the sight of him?

8. On the way to winning the FA Cup in 1970, Peter Osgood scored in every round. 51 years later nobody has repeated the feat. Which player had done so two years before in 1968?

9. Although Peter came back to Chelsea at the end of his career it didn't work out for him. Previously he had left for Southampton in March 1974 for £275,000 and while at that club won the FA Cup again in 1976. Which was the only other English club he played for?

10. A lot of fans know about Jeunesse Hautcharage even if they might not be able to spell it! As mentioned elsewhere, Chelsea beat them 21-0 on aggregate in the first round of the European Cup Winners' Cup in 1971. How many of those 21 goals did Peter Osgood score?

QUIZ No. 69

FULHAM ROAD FAVOURITES No. 10 – BOBBY TAMBLING

1. The top Chelsea goalscorer until Frank got in on the act, Bobby Tambling running at defences was a familiar sight throughout the 1960s at Stamford Bridge and his 164 league goals in 302 games was a great haul. Naturally, he scored in a 3-2 home win on his debut on 7 February 1959 against which fellow Londoners?

2. Strangely enough, his first cup goal for Chelsea came against the same opposition as Peter Osgood scored his first Chelsea goal against. Tambling scored in a 4-2 home win in the League Cup on 24 October 1960. Who was it against?

3. Chelsea finished bottom of the First Division in 1961/62 but it didn't stop the young Bobby Tambling scoring two hat-tricks inside a month against two clubs from the same city. They came in a 6-1 home win in September and a 5-3 away defeat in October. Which city's teams were involved?

4. In how many successive seasons did Bobby Tambling score in the FA Cup third or fourth round?

5. Bobby scored four goals in a game on four occasions. Two of those four timers were at Stamford Bridge against Portsmouth and Sunderland, the other two coming on other London grounds, the first when Chelsea won 4-1 in 1962 and the second when they prevailed 4-2 in 1964. Which two London clubs did he score four times against?

6. He went one better just once. He liked playing on this ground. In 1964/65 he scored there, and then in the following season he doubled his first effort. But he was merely warming up for the big one on 17 September 1966 when he netted five times in Chelsea's 6-2 away win. Which ground has a special memory for him?

7. Bobby Tambling scored just three European goals for Chelsea. The last one came against Morton in 1968/69, but in the previous season he had bagged both Chelsea's goals in a 2-2 first-leg Fairs Cup draw in which German city?

8. The last time he played for Chelsea was as a substitute in an away game on 30 March 1970 against a Midlands club that had been one of the original 12 members of the Football League in 1888. Who were they?

9. In that same year of 1970, which London club did he join for a fee of £40,000, going on to score 12 goals in 68 games for them?

10. Only Jimmy Greaves stands above him where league goals in a season are concerned. How many did he get in the promotion season of 1962/63?

QUIZ No. 70

FULHAM ROAD FAVOURITES No. 11 – JOHN TERRY

1) Arguably England's best post-war central defender, he was a legendary figure at Stamford Bridge for nearly 20 years and gave everything to the cause. The same club that he made his Chelsea debut against as a substitute in the League Cup on 28 October 1998 were also the club he celebrated his 400th game as Chelsea captain against on 31 December 2011. Who were they?

2) John Terry played for just three clubs in his career and they have all won the European Cup/Champions League at some point in their history. Chelsea and Aston Villa are two of them. Who is the third?

3) On 5 December 2001 Chelsea came out under the Stamford Bridge lights for the first time under JT's leadership, while on 18 October 2014 in an away game he led them for the 500th time. On each occasion their opponents were London clubs that begin with the same letter. Who were they?

4) On 25 November 2015 John Terry set a new record for Chelsea's fastest Champions League goal when he scored with a header after 90 seconds of a 5-0 away win against which club?

5) John scored his first England goal against Hungary on 30 May 2006 and his first goal as England captain later that same year on 16 August 2006 against Greece. They were both scored on the same ground and the second of them coincided with a new England manager's first game. What was the ground and who was the manager?

6) What was special about a goal John scored for England in a 1-1 draw with Brazil in 2007?

7) What was unusual about John Terry's performance in a 1-0 away win over Reading on 14 October 2006?

8) John Terry played his 717th and final Chelsea game amid emotional scenes at Stamford Bridge on 21 May 2017 in a game that Chelsea won 5-1. Who were they playing?

9) On which ground did John Terry play the last game of his career?

10) Who were the only club that John Terry scored against for two clubs?

QUIZ No. 71

FULHAM ROAD FAVOURITES No. 12 – GIANFRANCO ZOLA

1. Although he was probably the most loved of all Chelsea players by their supporters because of his brilliance on the ball, his bravery and his attitude on the pitch, supporters of other clubs liked him as well, which tells its own story. For all his longevity, he won only one league title and that was in his native Italy with which club?

2. Which two men who eventually managed Chelsea did Zola play for in Italy before he arrived in this country for £4.5 million in November 1996?

3. His first hat-trick came in a 4-0 Chelsea win on 29 November 1997 against which club in the Premier League?

4. He became the first Chelsea player to win the FWA Player of the Year award in which season?

5. Gianfranco Zola played a major part in Chelsea winning the FA Cup in 1997 with goals in four of the six rounds it took to win it. He found the net in a 3-0 third-round win over West Brom and in a 4-1 win in the fifth round over Portsmouth. However, his goal in a 4-2 fourth-round win, and another in Chelsea's 3-0 semi-final victory stood out from the rest with their brilliance. Which two clubs did Chelsea knock out?

6. Which two British countries did he score against for Italy, both in 1997, the first in a friendly in Palermo and the second in a World Cup qualifier in Britain?

7. The first two and the last letters of the manager who gave Zola his first cap in November 1991 against Norway are the same two first letters and last letter of the man Zola was assistant to at Chelsea after his retirement. Who are the two men?

8. Which English club has Zola lost to in a European Cup Winners' Cup final?

9. He scored his last goal for Chelsea on Easter Monday of 2003, and played his last game for the club on the final day of that season on 11 May 2003. The two teams Chelsea played in those games come from the same city. Which one?

10. Zola did get his hands on that European Cup Winners' Cup with Chelsea in 1998 when he scored the winning goal. Before he joined Chelsea he had won the UEFA Cup with Parma in 1995, and the team they beat in that final were also the team Zola played in the very last match of his career for Cagliari, scoring twice in the process. Who were they?

QUIZ No. 72

GOALKEEPERS - PART 1

1. He played over 200 times for Chelsea in all competitions including 26 league games when they won the league for the first time in 1954/55. Who was he?

2. Who was the only Chelsea goalkeeper to face two penalties in an FA Cup final?

3. Which Chelsea goalkeeper becomes very funny if you add two letters to the end of his name?

4. Who played in goal for Chelsea against Bruges and Manchester City in the quarter-final and semi-final of the European Cup Winners' Cup when Chelsea won it in 1970/71?

5. Alex Stepney went on to become a European Cup winner with Manchester United but played just once for Chelsea after his move from another London club in 1966. Which club did he come from and on which ground did he play his only game for Chelsea, which they won 3-0?

6. A popular Chelsea goalkeeper played 136 league games between 1983 and 1988 after his move from Wrexham. Who was he, with a bonus point if you spell his name correctly?

7. Who played in goal for Chelsea in their FA Cup final victory over Middlesbrough in 1997?

8. This slightly crazy keeper from Belgrade delighted and frustrated fans in equal measure in his 107 league appearances between 1979 and 1982. Who was he?

9. A member of the side that won the Full Members' Cup at Wembley in 1986, he turned out 71 times in the league for the Blues between 1982 and 1987. Who was he?

10. He sounds like a football ground, but he was the first goalkeeper to play for Chelsea in an FA Cup final when he was between the sticks for them in 1915, and made over 200 appearances in the league for them as well. Who was he?

QUIZ No. 73

GOALKEEPERS - PART 2

1. Which goalkeeper had already played five times for England while with Coventry City from Division Three South before his move to Chelsea in 1956, where he went on to play for them in 135 league games before a move to Derby County in 1961?

2. Which Dutchman guarded Chelsea's net on 175 occasions in all competitions between 1997 and 2003 when he left to join Stoke City?

3. Which Belgian goalkeeper played 126 league games for Chelsea between 2011 and 2018?

4. This man kept goal superbly for Chelsea from 1946 to 1952, making 143 league appearances for the club, but after his retirement he devoted most of the rest of his life to Chelsea as a trainer and physiotherapist. Who was this highly respected Chelsea character?

5. At the end of the 2019/20 season this Chelsea goalkeeper had played in 69 league games for the club but it was his infamous performance in the 2019 League Cup final against Manchester City that made headlines when he refused to leave the field after being substituted by his manager. Who was he?

6. Which Australian goalkeeper played 12 times for Chelsea in the 2013/14 season between spells at Fulham and Leicester City?

7. Which Italian goalkeeper played 142 league games for the Blues in the first nine years of this century before a move across London to Spurs?

8. Collectively, between 1906 and the outbreak of war Chelsea were well served by two goalkeepers who made 179 league appearances between them. The other thing they shared was the first four letters of their surnames. Who were they?

9. Chelsea signed Edouard Mendy in 2020. From which club did they buy him and which country does he represent in international football?

10. A Chelsea regular, playing 223 league games between 1926 and 1932, he was a key part of the promotion team in the 1929/30 season, missing just four games. Who was he?

QUIZ No. 74

GREENER GRASS - PART 1

All these players appeared in an FA Cup final for another club *before* they came to Stamford Bridge. Can you identify them?

1. Which player scored for Arsenal in the 1998 FA Cup final before joining Chelsea and several other clubs as well?

2. Which member of Southampton's FA Cup final team of 2003 later joined Chelsea?

3. Which Chelsea player had won the FA Cup before in 1964 with West Ham United?

4. Which Chelsea full-back had previously played in the 2008 FA Cup final for Portsmouth?

5. Which Chelsea goalkeeper had previously played against Liverpool in an FA Cup final in the 1980s?

6. Which member of Arsenal's successful FA Cup final sides of 2014 and 2015 went on to join Chelsea?

7. Which Chelsea man played for different clubs in successive FA Cup finals before coming to Stamford Bridge in 1958?

8. Which two outfield members of the Wimbledon team from the 1988 FA Cup final later moved to Chelsea?

9. Two ex-Manchester United cup finalists joined Chelsea; the first after playing in the 1979 FA Cup final and the second after appearing in finals for them in 1985, 1990 and 1994. Who were they?

10. Two midfielders, one from Arsenal and the other from Spurs, both wound up at Chelsea after cup final appearances elsewhere. The Arsenal man played in the 2005 final while the Spurs man appeared in the finals of 1981, 1982 and 1987. Who were the two players?

QUIZ No. 75

GREENER GRASS – PART 2

All these players appeared in an FA Cup final for another club *after* leaving Stamford Bridge. Can you identify them?

1. Which four ex-Chelsea men turned out for Spurs in an FA Cup final, all of them in the 1960s?

2. Which member of Chelsea's title-winning side of 1955 played in goal for Nottingham Forest in the 1959 FA Cup final?

3. Which ex-Chelsea winger was part of West Ham United's FA Cup-winning side of 1964?

4. Which two ex-Chelsea players were part of the successful Southampton team that won the FA Cup in 1976?

5. Which two ex-Blues played for Arsenal in FA Cup finals in the 1970s?

6. Which ex-Chelsea goalkeeper played for Watford in the 1984 FA Cup final?

7. Which ex-Chelsea man later played for a non-English club in an FA Cup final?

8. One ex-Chelsea player was in Manchester United's FA Cup final teams of 1976 and 1977 while another was in their 1983 FA Cup winning side. In this century two more ex-Chelsea players have gone on to represent Manchester United in FA Cup finals with surnames that start with the same three letters. Who are the four players in question?

9. Which ex-Blue didn't have to change his shirt colour when he played for Everton against Liverpool in the 1989 FA Cup final?

10. Which ex-Chelsea man was in the Liverpool team that lost to Wimbledon in the 1988 final?

QUIZ No. 76

HELPING HANDS
(POST-WAR OWN GOALS)

1. Which legendary Manchester City goalkeeper scored Chelsea's goal when they drew 1-1 at Maine Road on 25 February 1950?

2. Which future Chelsea manager contributed an own goal to Chelsea's 3-2 win at Deepdale against Preston North End on 22 October 1955?

3. The man who held the FA Cup aloft for Manchester City ten months before experienced his good fortune deserting him at Stamford Bridge on 9 March 1957 when his own goal was one of Chelsea's four in a 4-2 home win. Who was he?

4. On 20 April in that same year Chelsea beat Everton 5-1 at Stamford Bridge and one of their goals came from the Everton goalkeeper who shared his surname with a sports manufacturer. Who was he?

5. Five months before he had scored Luton's goal in their losing FA Cup final against Nottingham Forest, but now, on 17 October 1959 he was finding his own net to give Chelsea a 2-1 win in Bedfordshire. Who was he?

6. Near the end of the 1960/61 season Chelsea beat Arsenal 3-1 at Stamford Bridge, with one of the three coming from someone who would go on to manage both Arsenal and Spurs. Who was he?

7. On 15 October 1966 Chelsea came away from Old Trafford with a 1-1 draw courtesy of an own goal from which Scottish international?

8. In the penultimate game of the 1977/78 season, QPR lost 3-1 at Stamford Bridge. One of Chelsea's goals came from a very popular ex-Chelsea player. Who was he? Even more popular after that!

9. When Chelsea beat Bolton Wanderers 4-3 at Stamford Bridge on 14 October 1978, one of their goals was an own goal by a future England manager. Who was he?

THE ULTIMATE CHELSEA QUIZ BOOK

10. On 19 April 1976 Chelsea's goal in a 1-1 draw at Charlton Athletic came from one of the home side's defenders. On 14 January 1984 Chelsea's 2-1 win at Derby County was assisted by an own goal from the home goalkeeper. The two players being generous to the Blues have names that rhyme with each other and are both found on trees. Who were they?

QUIZ No. 77

HELPING HANDS
(OWN GOALS IN THE PREMIER LEAGUE ERA)

1. Three goalkeepers from clubs in the North West were unfortunate enough to score for Chelsea in season 2006/07. They played for Everton, Wigan Athletic and Bolton Wanderers. Who were the three goalkeepers?

2. Which Manchester City defender who was quite partial to the odd own goal got one of Chelsea's in their 2-0 away win on 5 April 2008?

3. Chelsea didn't need a helping hand when they won 5-0 at Middlesbrough on 18 October 2008, but they got one anyway with an own goal from which player?

4. Which Bournemouth defender put through his own net when Chelsea beat them 3-0 on Boxing Day of 2016?

5. Which Fulham defender gave Chelsea a belated Christmas present on 28 December 2009 in the derby that the Blues won 2-1 at Stamford Bridge?

6. Which central defender with a Premier League winners' medal to his name put through his own net against Chelsea while with both Coventry City and Bolton Wanderers in the first two years of this century?

7. Which ex-Chelsea man, who did have a knack of scoring in the wrong end, did Chelsea a favour in that regard while with Leicester City in 1999?

8. Which Manchester City player, on 5 December 2009, gave Chelsea a goal with one hand and then took it away with the other by scoring for his own team in their 2-1 win?

9. Which Manchester United defender contributed an own goal to Chelsea's cause in a 3-3 draw between the clubs at Stamford Bridge on 5 February 2012?

10. Which Middlesbrough defender put through his own goal when his team were beaten 3-0 in London on 10 February 2007?

QUIZ No. 78

IF THE CAP FITS – PART 1 – ENGLAND

1. Which two Chelsea players who both wore the number four on the back of their shirt played just once for their country, the first in 1955 and the second in 1967?

2. Who among the following players is the only Chelsea player to reach double figures in his caps total? – Roy Bentley, Frank Blunstone, Peter Bonetti, Kerry Dixon or Peter Osgood.

3. Besides Peter Bonetti, who is the only other goalkeeper in the post-war era to be capped for England while at the club?

4. What is the link between Peter Brabrook, Peter Sillett and Bobby Tambling where caps are concerned?

5. Which full-back received one England cap in 1963 while with Chelsea?

6. Who is the only post-war Chelsea international to be capped with four other clubs as well?

7. What is the only surname that has appeared twice among Chelsea's England internationals this century?

8. Add one letter to the name of a player who was capped while with Chelsea this century and you produce another Chelsea player who played for England in the last century. Who are the two men?

9. Dennis Wise, Graeme Le Saux, Bobby Tambling and Glen Johnson all scored the same number of goals for England. How many?

10. Who is the only post-war player capped for England while at Chelsea to also be capped while with a foreign club?

QUIZ No. 79

IF THE CAP FITS - PART 2 - SCOTLAND

1. Doug Rougvie was a popular defender at Stamford Bridge between 1984 and 1987 and won one cap for Scotland during his time with the club. True or false?

2. He sounds Welsh but won 48 caps for Scotland before coming to Chelsea in 1960 at the end of a very distinguished career north of the border. Who was he?

3. Which two players with surnames beginning with 'S' won caps for Scotland, the first in the mid-1980s and the second a decade later?

4. Charlie Cooke was a class act and won 16 caps for Scotland. He had two spells at Chelsea, the first from 1966 to 1972 and the second from 1973 to 1978. Which two clubs did Chelsea sign him from?

5. Which striker was capped for Scotland in the late 1980s while at Stamford Bridge and in the next decade received further caps while at Spurs and Glasgow Rangers?

6. Which Chelsea defender who came back to the club in a different capacity after his playing career made six appearances for Scotland between 1988 and 1994?

7. Pat Nevin was a popular ball player with Chelsea in the 1980s and won 28 caps for his country. Which two other clubs did he win caps with besides Chelsea?

8. Eddie McCreadie won 23 Scottish caps while with Chelsea in the 1960s. Which Scottish club sold him to Chelsea in 1962?

9. Which 1990s Chelsea player won 46 Scottish caps while with Chelsea, Celtic and Derby County?

10. He played 72 times for his country but his time at Chelsea in 1991/92 was a small interlude between substantial spells at Motherwell and Celtic. Who was he?

QUIZ No. 80

IF THE CAP FITS – PART 3 – WALES, NORTHERN IRELAND AND THE REPUBLIC OF IRELAND

1. Who is the only Welshman to be capped while at Chelsea who had previously won the European Cup with another club?

2. Which Northern Ireland striker played for Chelsea 152 times between 1987 and 1992?

3. Which Republic of Ireland international was influential in the Chelsea midfield between 1990 and 1993 in over 100 league games for the club?

4. Which Welshman did Chelsea pay Cardiff City a club-record fee for in 1961, selling him on to Manchester United for the same fee two years later?

5. Two Northern Ireland internationals played for Chelsea in the early 1950s, one up front and the other at the back. Both left the club before the title success of 1955 and both their names begin with the letter 'D'. Who were they?

6. Which Republic of Ireland international front man played 40 league games for Chelsea between 1992 and 1994?

7. Who are the only two goalkeepers to be capped for Wales post-war while at Chelsea?

8. Which Republic of Ireland winger played without the ubiquitous agent, 125 times in all competitions for Chelsea between 2003 and 2006?

9. Which midfielder that Chelsea loaned to Sheffield United in 2020 has represented Wales on 19 occasions?

10. Which popular centre-half at Stamford Bridge between 1969 and 1978 won 19 caps for the Republic of Ireland?

IF THE CAP FITS – PART 4 – OVERSEAS PLAYERS

Which countries do the following Chelsea players represent?

1. Tore Andre Flo

2. Marcos Alonso

3. Antonio Rudiger

4. Asmir Begovic

5. John Obi Mikel

6. Loic Remy

7. Dan Petrescu

8. Andreas Christensen

9. Christian Pulisic

10. Willy Caballero

QUIZ No. 82

IF THE CAP FITS – PART 5 – MORE OVERSEAS PLAYERS

Which countries do the following Chelsea players represent?

1. Ed de Goey

2. Roberto Di Matteo

3. Branislav Ivanovic

4. Mark Bosnich

5. Hakim Ziyech

6. Mateo Kovacic

7. Ramires

8. Romelu Lukaku

9. Paulo Ferreira

10. Salomon Kalou

MANAGERS

1. Which country managed Chelsea for one winning game in 2015?

2. Who is the only man to manage Chelsea in two different centuries?

3. Chelsea have been managed by two men whose first name and surname begin with the same letter, one either side of the Second World War and the other more recently. Who are they?

4. Chelsea have won the FA Cup eight times, but no manager has won it more than once. True or false?

5. How many times has an Englishman won the FA Cup as Chelsea's manager?

6. Which nation has provided Chelsea with the most managers, Scotland or Italy?

7. Six Chelsea managers have won European trophies while at the club. Two of them share the first letter of their surnames. Who are they?

8. Which two managers in the current century have had two spells of management at the club?

9. Who was the first Chelsea manager to win the League Cup?

10. Which two Chelsea managers achieved promotion to the top flight in the 1980s?

QUIZ No. 84

MULTIPLE CHOICE

1. In an away game on Boxing Day of 1999 Chelsea became the first club to field a completely non-British team in league football. Who were their opponents that day?
    A) Southampton   B) Derby County   C) Middlesbrough
    D) Coventry City

2. When Chelsea won 3-1 at Stamford Bridge on 18 December 1954, one of their goals went into the record books as a joint own goal when two players, Stan Milburn and Jack Froggatt, struck the ball together into their own net. Who were the visitors that day?
    A) Portsmouth   B) Newcastle United   C) Leicester City
    D) Burnley

3. Chelsea broke the clean-sheets record for a 38-match top-flight campaign when they achieved 25 of them in 2004/05. Only one club at that time had achieved more, with 28, but that came in a 42-game programme. Who were that club?
    A) Arsenal   B) Liverpool   C) Manchester United   D) Wolves

4. In the 2021/22 season Chelsea became the sixth club still playing league football to appear in three successive FA Cup finals. The previous five were Arsenal, Blackburn Rovers, Everton, Manchester United and West Bromwich Albion. Which one of those five has managed to do it twice?

5. The best top-flight home record in a 38-match season is 18 wins and a draw in 19 games. Besides Chelsea, it has been achieved by Liverpool, Manchester City, Manchester United and one other club. Which one?
    A) Newcastle United   B) Arsenal   C) Spurs
    D) Nottingham Forest

6. Dave Beasant played in goal for Chelsea 133 times in league football, which places the Londoners third in the appearances list of the player's nine clubs. Which one of these four did he play for in more league games than he did for Chelsea?
   A) Portsmouth B) Newcastle United C) Southampton
   D) Nottingham Forest

7. Which one of these five men has not played in an FA Cup final for Chelsea in two different centuries?
   A) Dennis Wise B) John Terry C) Roberto Di Matteo
   D) Gianfranco Zola E) Frank Lampard

8. Three Chelsea players appear in the top ten sendings-off list. Which one of these four is not on that list?
   A) Vinnie Jones B) Ron Harris C) Dennis Wise
   D) Roy McDonough

9. Over two seasons in 2008 Chelsea set a record for top-flight consecutive away wins with how many?
   A) 9 B) 10 C) 11 D) 12

10. Which Manchester United player was sent off in the Charity Shield against Chelsea in 2000 at Wembley?
    A) Roy Keane B) Paul Scholes C) Gary Neville
    D) David Beckham

QUIZ No. 85

OPENING DAYS

1. It was the opening day of all opening days, Chelsea's first game in the Football League Division Two on 2 September 1905. Which northern club beat them 1-0 in front of 7,000 fans?

2. After winning the Premier League in 2004/05, Chelsea retained the title with nine straight wins to start the following season. However, that run didn't look likely on the opening day at Wigan until which player grabbed the game's only goal in the 93rd minute?

3. Chelsea's start to their defence of the Premier League trophy they had won in 2016/17 was less successful. In a home game on 12 August 2017 in which two Chelsea players received red cards they were beaten 3-2 by which northern club?

4. On 14 August 2010 which Chelsea player hit the ground running by scoring three of their goals when they won 6-0 at Stamford Bridge?

5. On 22 August 1959 the 43,000 inside Stamford Bridge were treated to the club's first-ever 4-4 draw on opening day. Which club from Lancashire were the visitors?

6. Which player scored an opening-day hat-trick against Chelsea for Coventry City on 9 August 1997?

7. Which team from Lancashire did Chelsea beat 4-3 on the opening day of the first season back after the Second World War, and then lose 2-0 to on the opening day of 1955/56 as defending title holders, both games being played at Stamford Bridge?

8. It only took until the second opening day in Chelsea's history and the first on their own ground for them to record their biggest-ever league win by 9-2. Who were they playing and who scored five of the goals?

9. They had to wait until 28 August 1937 to see something approaching that score again on an opening day at Stamford Bridge. Which northern club did they beat 6-1 that day?

10. On 7 August 1999 Chelsea fans were treated to a 4-0 opening day win and a goal of great brilliance and imagination concocted by the skills of Gus Poyet and Gianfranco Zola. Which club's players could only stand and watch?

QUIZ No. 86

OTHER COMPETITIONS

1. Which competition did Chelsea win in 1960 and 1961 before waiting half a century to win it again, and then land it seven times in the next nine years?

2. It didn't have great status but the first Full Members' Cup final on 23 March 1986 was a treat for the 67,000 who turned up to watch it, Chelsea taking the trophy with a 5-4 win. Who did they beat and which Chelsea man scored a hat-trick?

3. Four years later the competition had a new name and was now known as the Zenith Data Systems Cup, and this time over 76,000 saw Chelsea win it 1-0. Who did they play and who scored the winning goal?

4. These competitions seem to have more names than Prince! The traditional curtain raiser to the season at Wembley between the League Champions and FA Cup holders used to be called the Charity Shield but now goes by the name of the Community Shield. Whatever, Chelsea have been involved in it 13 times against six different clubs. Four of them are Arsenal, Liverpool and both Manchester clubs. Who are the other two?

5. Chelsea made their first visit to Wembley to contest the League South Cup final of 1944 during the Second World War. They lost 3-1 to another London club but came back the following year to win the trophy against a different club from the capital by 2-0. Who were their two opponents?

6. 175,000 people watched those two wartime finals. Which rather significant figure with a few things on his mind met the teams before the first of those two finals?

7. Now we come to the largely pointless competitions dreamed up by the likes of FIFA and UEFA. Chelsea have made one appearance in the so-called Club World Cup. It came in 2012 when they went down 1-0 to which Brazilian club?

8. Chelsea's first two appearances in the European Super Cup came in 1998 and 2012. They won the first and lost the second against two teams from the same city and both games were played on the same ground. What was the city and the venue for the matches?

9. In 2013 and 2019 Chelsea drew 2-2 after extra time in that same competition, losing both penalty shoot-outs by the same 5-4 score. Who were their two opponents in those games?

10. In which two cities were those games played to little or no purpose?

QUIZ No. 87

POT LUCK

1. The Sillett brothers, Peter and John, played nearly 400 times for Chelsea between them and were also associated in different capacities with two other clubs. Who were they?

2. Which Chelsea player received a red card in the 2017 Community Shield against Arsenal at Wembley?

3. Thomas Tuchel is the first Chelsea manager with a surname beginning with 'T'. True or false?

4. Who is the only Chelsea player who has gone on to manage a country to win the World Cup?

5. Which is the closest ground to Stamford Bridge on which an FA Cup final has been played?

6. Since its inception in the 2009/10 season, Chelsea's two wins in Europa League finals is the best record of any English club. Which four other English clubs have appeared in the final of that competition?

7. Brothers Graham and Ray Wilkins both played for other London clubs, one in each case. Which two clubs were involved?

8. Besides being Chelsea's first manager, what is John Tait Robertson also famous for?

9. What was the year of the only major final where the Chelsea team had two brothers in the line-up, and who were those brothers?

10. Which town in Livingston County, New York, contains the names of two Chelsea players, one from the current team and the other who played over 100 league games between 1996 and 2003?

QUIZ No. 88

STAMFORD BRIDGE

1. Stamford Bridge opened as a sporting venue on 28 April 1877. Which sport was it home to in its earliest days?

2. Which football club were due, in 1904, to rent Stamford Bridge for £1,500 a year until negotiations fell through at the last minute?

3. Chelsea moved from formation to league football in record time and their first game at Stamford Bridge was a triumph for Jimmy Windridge who scored a hat-trick in a 5-1 win over which club on 11 September 1905?

4. Stamford Bridge was honoured with three successive FA Cup finals between 1920 and 1922 before the new Wembley Stadium took over from 1923 onwards. One club appeared in more than one final in those years. Who were they?

5. The official attendance record at Stamford Bridge is 82,905, and was set on 12 October 1935 in a 1-1 draw against which club?

6. England have played four full internationals on the pitch, the last of them against Switzerland in 1946 deemed unofficial owing to its status as a wartime game. Scotland and Wales failed to score against England in two of the other three, so which country, in going down 4-3 there on 7 December 1932, have been the only official visitors to score against England on the ground?

7. Which Chelsea player scored for England in the game against Switzerland mentioned in the previous question?

8. Believe it or not, Stamford Bridge has been home to athletics, baseball, cricket, rifle-shooting, rugby league and speedway over the years. Which sport at the venue ran from 1933 to 1968 and enjoyed immense popularity in the years just after the Second World War?

9. The strength of Chelsea's ambition was shown by their decision before they had kicked a ball in their ground to commission a new stand along the eastern side of the ground to accommodate 5,000 spectators. They turned to an architect who was starting to make a name for himself in this area. Who was he?

10. Stamford Bridge was notable for the amazing height and shape of its vast terracing. They were fortunate in being able to build so high that a vast excavation was taking place nearby with the construction of a new London Underground line, with Chelsea using that material as the base for the new terracing. Which underground line was being built?

QUIZ No. 89

TRANSFERS - 1945-60

All the following players joined Chelsea in this period from another club and left the Londoners to try their luck elsewhere, in most cases within the timespan above. Can you identify the player in each case?

1. Which popular centre-forward came from Everton in 1945 and left for Notts County in 1947 after scoring 30 times in 42 league games for Chelsea?

2. He played 181 league games for Chelsea, scoring 59 goals, after arriving from Brighton in 1952. He eventually left for Crystal Palace in 1958. Who was he?

3. Which wing-half came to Stamford Bridge from Reading in 1959, making 76 league appearances before a move to QPR in 1962?

4. This player's Chelsea career comprised 112 league games and 34 goals and came between 1952 and 1958, sandwiched between two spells at Southend United. Who was he?

5. This winger's entire league career took place in London. He joined Chelsea from West Ham United in 1950 and 158 league games and 37 goals later, in 1956, he joined Brentford after gaining a league winner's medal with Chelsea the year before. Who was he?

6. This wing-half played over 100 games for QPR before his move to Chelsea in 1955. After 26 league outings he moved on to Coventry City and made over 100 appearances there as well. Who was he?

7. Later in his career he won an FA Cup winner's medal with Nottingham Forest, but he joined Chelsea from Leyton Orient in 1949 and moved on to Burnley against most fans' wishes in 1953 after scoring 12 goals in 146 league outings for the Blues. Who was he?

8. Capped while with Spurs, this inside-forward joined Chelsea in 1959 as part of the deal that took Les Allen to Tottenham. Before he joined a potent Brentford attack in 1961 he played in 46 league games for Chelsea, scoring six times. Who was he?

9. This scorer of 17 league goals in 39 games for Chelsea between 1959 and 1961 came to the club in the deal that took Cliff Huxford to Southampton, and then moved on to Gillingham. Who was he?

10. A legendary Scottish player, who had played as a guest for Chelsea during the war, joined them from Hearts in 1946 and returned to that club two years later, but not before playing 98 games at inside-forward for Chelsea to the delight of their supporters. As a manager he led Hearts to the Scottish Cup in 1956 and was awarded the OBE. Who was he?

TRANSFERS - THE 1960s

A different approach this time. You are given the name of a Chelsea player from the 1960s and are required to name the club he came from and the club he left Chelsea for. Here are the ten.

1. Joe Kirkup

2. Tony Hateley

3. David Webb

4. Alan Birchenall

5. George Graham

6. Bobby Evans

7. Andy Malcolm

8. Frank Upton

9. Derek Kevan

10. Alan Young

TRANSFERS – THE 1970s AND 1980s – PART 1

You are given the year these players joined Chelsea. From which clubs did they arrive in each case?

1. Tony Dorigo – 1987

2. Chris Garland – 1971

3. Nigel Spackman – 1983

4. Steve Kember – 1971

5. Dennis Rofe – 1980

6. David Speedie – 1982

7. Keith Weller – 1970

8. Pat Nevin – 1983

9. Bill Garner – 1972

10. Gordon Durie – 1986

TRANSFERS – THE 1970s AND 1980s – PART 2

You are given the year these players left Chelsea. Which clubs did they go to in each case?

1. Kenny Swain – 1978

2. John Dempsey – 1978

3. Colin Lee – 1987

4. Gary Chivers – 1983

5. Mike Fillery – 1983

6. Ian Britton – 1982

7. Gary Locke – 1983

8. Peter Rhoades-Brown – 1984

9. Mickey Thomas – 1985

10. Chris Hutchings – 1983

QUIZ No. 93

TRANSFERS - THE 1990s
PART 1 - 'THE DOMESTIC SCENE'

Who did the following play for before arriving at Chelsea?

1. Scott Minto

2. Paul Furlong

3. John Spencer

4. Mark Stein

5. Dan Petrescu

6. Gavin Peacock

7. Tony Cascarino

8. Glenn Hoddle

9. Vinnie Jones

10. Robert Fleck

QUIZ No. 94

TRANSFERS - THE 1990s
PART 2 - 'THE FOREIGN LEGION'

Chelsea were among the earliest dabblers in the overseas market during the 1990s. From which European clubs did they obtain the following players?

1. Ed de Goey

2. Celestine Babayaro

3. Ruud Gullit

4. Gianluca Vialli

5. Marcel Desailly

6. Frank Lebouef

7. Gianfranco Zola

8. Gus Poyet

9. Roberto Di Matteo

10. Dmitri Kharine

QUIZ No. 95

TRANSFERS - 2000-20
PART 1 - 'THE DOMESTIC SCENE'

1. Which full-back joined Chelsea from West Ham United for £6 million in 2003?

2. Which forward came to Stamford Bridge from Newcastle United in January 2013?

3. Which midfielder went to Chelsea from Charlton Athletic in January 2004?

4. Which versatile performer made his way to Chelsea from Wigan Athletic in August 2012?

5. Which playmaker left Liverpool for Chelsea in July 2010?

6. Which full-back's move from Arsenal to Chelsea took place extremely acrimoniously in 2006, and which player's move to Arsenal was part of the deal?

7. Which Blackburn Rovers winger did Chelsea pay £17 million for in July 2003?

8. Two forwards left Manchester City for Chelsea, the first in July 2005 and the second in July 2009. Who were they?

9. Which Southampton defender moved to Chelsea in July 2003, and which Chelsea player went in the opposite direction as part of the deal?

10. Bolton Wanderers provided Chelsea with three players during this period, the first in 2000 for £4 million, the second in 2008 for £15 million, and the third in 2012 for £7 million. Who were the three players?

TRANSFERS - 2000-20
PART 2 - 'THE FOREIGN LEGION'

Which clubs sold the following players to Chelsea?

1. Juan Mata

2. Romelu Lukaku

3. Marcos Alonso

4. Andreas Christensen

5. Michael Ballack

6. Andriy Shevchenko

7. Kurt Zouma

8. Diego Costa

9. Jorginho

10. Christian Pulisic

QUIZ No. 97

TRANSFERS - 2000-20
PART 3 - 'MORE FOREIGN AFFAIRS'

1. Which club sold Michael Essien and Florent Malouda to Chelsea?

2. Which club sold Antonio Rudiger and Emerson to Chelsea?

3. From which club did Claude Makelele and Mateo Kovacic arrive at Stamford Bridge?

4. Genk provided Chelsea with an excellent goalkeeper and probably the greatest player to slip through Chelsea's fingers. Who were the two men?

5. Which club sold Chelsea Nemanja Matic, Ramires and David Luiz first time around?

6. From which club did Chelsea buy Mateja Kezman, Arjen Robben and Alex?

7. From which club did Chelsea buy Hakim Ziyech?

8. Chelsea signed two players from Barcelona, one in June 2008 and the other in August 2015, whose names both end with the same vowel. Who were they?

9. Which two players left Porto for Chelsea in 2004?

10. From which club did Chelsea buy Mario Stanic and Adrian Mutu in the early years of this century?

QUIZ No. 98

TRUE OR FALSE

1. Graham Roberts was successful 12 times from the penalty spot for Chelsea in the 1988/89 league season. True or false?

2. By reaching the FA Cup semi-final in 2021/22 Chelsea drew alongside Everton on 26 semi-final appearances each. True or false?

3. Where England, Scotland, Wales and the two Ireland's are concerned, the only two Chelsea players to reach 100 caps in their career are Frank Lampard and Ashley Cole. True or false?

4. Kerry Dixon and Gianluca Vialli have both scored four goals in a league fixture against Barnsley. True or false?

5. Rotherham United are the only club to beat Chelsea by six goals at the second level of English football. True or false?

6. George Hilsdon, Jimmy Greaves and Bobby Tambling were the only players to score five times in a league game for Chelsea in the 20th century. True or false?

7. Up to and including the 2021/22 season, Chelsea have played in more FA Cup finals this century than any other club. True or false?

8. In the 1950s Chelsea both lost and won 6-5 in league matches at Stamford Bridge. True or false?

9. The two clubs that contested the famous 1923 FA Cup final at Wembley were the only two clubs that Chelsea drew with 5-5 in the 20th century. True or false?

10. Leeds City in 1907 were the first club to draw an FA Cup tie with Chelsea. True or false?

QUIZ No. 99

VENUES

1. What is the only ground that Chelsea have lost an FA Cup final on but never won one there?

2. Which is the only ground outside of Wembley that Chelsea have won and lost an FA Cup final on?

3. By 1915 which city had seen Chelsea play an FA Cup semi-final on two of its grounds?

4. Which is the only ground that Chelsea have played on in the second leg of a League Cup final?

5. Which two Yorkshire grounds did Chelsea play a semi-final on between the wars?

6. What is the most southerly city that Chelsea have won a major European trophy in?

7. What is the most northerly city that Chelsea have won a major European trophy in?

8. Chelsea have won and lost a Champions League final in two cities beginning with the same letter. Which two?

9. In which city did Chelsea win the Europa League for the first time in 2013?

10. UEFA excelled itself for the Europa League final of 2019 between Chelsea and Arsenal which could have been played a few stops on the tube from either club. Instead, supporters were asked to pay four-figure sums and travel halfway round the world to Azerbaijan to see their team. In which city was the match held?

QUIZ No. 100

WEMBLEY, WEMBLEY! (WINNING FA CUP SEMI-FINALS)

Chelsea have won 16 of the 26 FA Cup semi-finals they have contested. Here are some questions about those joyous occasions.

1. Who are the only club that Chelsea have beaten in more than one FA Cup semi-final?

2. Who are the most northerly and most southerly sides that Chelsea have knocked out at the semi-final stage of the FA Cup?

3. Which beaten FA Cup semi-finalists are the nearest geographically to Stamford Bridge?

4. Which two players with surnames beginning with 'P' have scored twice in an FA Cup semi-final for Chelsea?

5. Which two clubs have Chelsea beaten 5-1 in an FA Cup semi-final?

6. In winning those 16 semi-finals Chelsea have scored just once from the penalty spot. Who took it?

7. Who are the only club that scored twice when losing an FA Cup semi-final to Chelsea?

8. Who are the only two Chelsea players to score in successive seasons in winning FA Cup semi-finals?

9. Which four league grounds have Chelsea won an FA Cup semi-final on?

10. Six Chelsea players with a surname starting with an 'H' have scored for them in a winning FA Cup semi-final. How many can you name?

ANSWERS

QUIZ No. 1 - ANYTHING GOES
1. Surrey
2. Manchester United
3. Aston Villa
4. Nine
5. He was the first American to score in an FA Cup final
6. Oscar
7. Daniel Sturridge and Glen Johnson
8. They are the only men to play for three different clubs in an FA Cup final
9. Alan Hudson
10. Willie Foulke

QUIZ No. 2 - ASSORTED BLUES
1. Ron Greenwood
2. Jack Cock
3. Albert Murray
4. Henry Ford
5. Marvin Hinton
6. George Mills
7. Dick Spence
8. John Boyle
9. John Harris
10. Joe McLaughlin

QUIZ No. 3 - BLUES SEEING RED
1. Babayaro and Ballack
2. Carvalho and Costa
3. Cech and Courtois
4. Mikel and Malouda
5. Terry and Torres
6. Huth
7. Gallas
8. Robben
9. Essien
10. Drogba

QUIZ No. 4 - A BRIDGE TOO FAR (LOSING FA CUP SEMI-FINALS)
1. Newcastle United
2. Jimmy Croal
3. Arsenal
4. White Hart Lane
5. Liverpool and Sheffield Wednesday
6. Manchester United
7. Didier Drogba
8. Demba Ba
9. Birmingham – three at Villa Park and one at St. Andrews
10. 2-1 – four times

QUIZ No. 5 - CHELSEA IN EUROPE - 1958-72 (CLUBS)
1. Denmark
2. Wiener Sport-Club
3. 11,000
4. TSV Munchen 1860
5. 60
6. DWS Amsterdam
7. Bulgaria
8. Bruges

9. Manchester City
10. Luxembourg and Sweden

QUIZ No. 6 - CHELSEA IN EUROPE - 1958-72 (PLAYERS)
1. Jimmy Greaves
2. Peter Brabrook
3. Trick question – they were two own goals
4. Terry Venables
5. George Graham
6. Barry Bridges
7. Alan Birchenall
8. Hollins, Hinton and Hutchinson
9. Peter Osgood
10. John Dempsey

QUIZ No. 7 - CHELSEA IN EUROPE - 1994-2000
1. Czech Republic
2. A Chelsea v Arsenal European final
3. Tromso and Vialli
4. Zola
5. Villa Park
6. Barcelona
7. AC Milan and Lazio
8. Leboeuf
9. Flo
10. Galatasaray

QUIZ No. 8 - CHELSEA IN EUROPE - 2000-04
1. St. Gallen
2. Panucci
3. Gudjohnsen
4. Hapoel Tel Aviv and Viking Stavanger
5. Gallas
6. Besiktas
7. Stuttgart
8. Arsenal
9. Monaco
10. Lampard

QUIZ No. 9 - CHELSEA IN EUROPE - 2004-07
1. Terry
2. Eto'o and Belletti
3. Ballack and Pizarro
4. Werder Bremen
5. Drogba
6. Four games – in front 2-1 with one draw
7. Deco and Gudjohnsen
8. Three
9. Joe Cole
10. Daniel Agger

QUIZ NO. 10 - CHELSEA IN EUROPE - 2007-10
1. Rosenborg, Bourdeaux and Atletico Madrid
2. Fenerbache and Liverpool

3. Drogba and Anelka
4. Terry
5. Five years and 4-4
6. Ivanovic and Torres
7. Kalou
8. Anelka
9. Panucci
10. Inter Milan

QUIZ NO. 11 - CHELSEA IN EUROPE - 2010-13

1. Manchester United
2. Anelka
3. Napoli
4. Ramires and Torres
5. Mata and Drogba
6. Robben and Drogba
7. Oscar and Willian
8. Benfica
9. Moses
10. Luiz and Ivanovic

QUIZ NO. 12 - CHELSEA IN EUROPE - 2013-17

1. PSG
2. Schalke
3. Lampard
4. Atletico Madrid
5. Basle
6. Maribor
7. Maccabi Tel Aviv
8. Willian
9. Galatasaray
10. They couldn't be knocked out because they weren't in Europe that season

QUIZ NO. 13 - CHELSEA IN EUROPE - 2017-20

1. Quarabag and nine
2. Barcelona
3. Loftus-Cheek and Giroud
4. Hudson-Odoi
5. Malmo and Slavia Prague
6. Eintracht Frankfurt
7. Giroud – it was against his old club, Arsenal
8. Ajax
9. Remy
10. Atletico Madrid and Real Madrid; when Chelsea won at Porto in the first leg of the quarter-final the game was played in Seville, but they played in Porto in the final itself

QUIZ NO. 14 - CHELSEA IN THE FA CUP FINAL - PART 1

1. True
2. Arsenal
3. Middlesbrough
4. Everton and Liverpool
5. Manchester United and Liverpool
6. Leeds United

7. Di Matteo and Saha
8. Moses and Kovacic
9. Middlesbrough and Portsmouth
10. Hazard

QUIZ NO. 15 - CHELSEA IN THE FA CUP FINAL - PART 2

1. Mark Hughes
2. Bobby Tambling
3. Jack Charlton, Eric Cantona and Andy Carroll
4. David Webb
5. Frank Lampard
6. Cook and Kitchen
7. Roberto Di Matteo
8. Peter Houseman and Ian Hutchinson
9. Glenn Hoddle and Craig Burley
10. Eddie Newton

QUIZ NO. 16 - CHELSEA IN THE FA CUP - 1905-39

1. Southampton
2. Newcastle United, Birmingham City, Cardiff City, Millwall and Crystal Palace
3. The First Battalion Grenadiers
4. Crystal Palace
5. Sheffield United, Aston Villa, Cardiff City, Arsenal and Newcastle United
6. Sheffield Wednesday
7. Bournemouth
8. Swindon Town
9. George Hilsdon
10. Grimsby Town

QUIZ NO. 17 - CHELSEA IN THE FA CUP - 1945-60

1. Tommy Lawton
2. Burnley
3. St. Andrews
4. Bobby Smith
5. Ken Armstrong and Peter Sillett
6. Roy Bentley
7. Aston Villa
8. Arsenal
9. Darlington
10. Arsenal and West Bromwich Albion

QUIZ No. 18 - CHELSEA IN CUP COMPETITIONS - 1960-70

1. Crewe Alexandra
2. Liverpool
3. Preston North End
4. Peter Osgood
5. Bobby Tambling
6. Millwall
7. Doncaster Rovers
8. Carlisle United
9. Peter Houseman
10. Workington

QUIZ No. 19 - CHELSEA IN CUP COMPETITIONS - 1970-80
1. Manchester
2. Bolton Wanderers
3. Tommy Baldwin
4. Orient
5. Spurs and Norwich City
6. Fog
7. Arsenal, QPR and Crystal Palace
8. Newport County
9. No player scored more than once
10. Stoke City

QUIZ No. 20 - CHELSEA IN CUP COMPETITIONS - 1980-90
1. Sunderland and Norwich City
2. Cardiff City
3. Wrexham
4. Leicester City
5. Mike Fillery
6. Kerry Dixon
7. David Speedie
8. Gordon Durie
9. Millwall
10. Scarborough and Scunthorpe United

QUIZ No. 21 - CHELSEA IN CUP COMPETITIONS - 1990-2000
1. Oxford United
2. Gavin Peacock
3. Millwall and Newcastle United
4. Frank Leboeuf
5. Middlesbrough
6. They won both shoot-outs by the same score of 4-1
7. Gianluca Vialli
8. Hull City
9. Four
10. 5-0

QUIZ No. 22 - CHELSEA IN LEAGUE CUP FINALS
1. Gordon Banks
2. Mateja Kezman
3. Eddie McCreadie, Frank Sinclair and John Terry
4. Dimitar Berbatov
5. Bobby Tambling, Peter Osgood, Roberto Di Matteo, Didier Drogba and Diego Costa
6. Spurs and Liverpool
7. Leicester City
8. They won two and lost one
9. Liverpool and Manchester City
10. Middlesbrough

QUIZ No. 23 - CHELSEA IN THE LEAGUE - 1905-39
1. Burslem Port Vale
2. They didn't draw any of them, winning 18 and losing one
3. 17-2-0
4. Henry Ford

5. They failed to win away
6. Third
7. 13
8. Blackpool
9. Dick Spence and Joe Bambrick
10. Joe Payne

QUIZ No. 24 - CHELSEA IN THE LEAGUE - 1946-60
1. Tommy Lawton
2. Ken Armstrong
3. Everton and Sheffield Wednesday
4. Manchester City
5. Derek Saunders and Eric Parsons
6. Sheffield Wednesday
7. Manchester City
8. Frank Blunstone and Roy Bentley
9. Reg Matthews
10. Jimmy Greaves

QUIZ No. 25 - CHELSEA IN THE LEAGUE - THE 1960s
1. February and Cardiff City
2. John Mortimore and Terry Venables
3. Sunderland
4. 7-0
5. Ron Harris
6. Jimmy Greaves and George Graham
7. Ninth
8. Tommy Baldwin and David Webb
9. One
10. John Hollins and Peter Houseman

QUIZ No. 26 - CHELSEA IN THE LEAGUE - THE 1970s
1. Carlisle United and Birmingham City
2. Keith Weller, Clive Walker and Ray Wilkins
3. 18
4. Steve Finnieston
5. Unbeaten at home
6. Chris Garland
7. Tommy Ord
8. Ray Wilkins and Gary Locke
9. Orient and Lee Frost
10. 24

QUIZ No. 27 - CHELSEA IN THE LEAGUE - THE 1980s
1. November – hard to believe but true
2. Colin Lee
3. Bolton Wanderers
4. Bobby Tambling
5. 1-1
6. Watford
7. Oxford United
8. Crystal Palace
9. Colin Pates
10. Millwall and Kerry Dixon

QUIZ No. 28 - CHELSEA IN THE LEAGUE - THE 1990s
1. 11th
2. Graham Stuart, John Spencer and Mark Stein
3. Derby County 4 Chelsea 6 and Nottingham Forest 7 Chelsea 0
4. Andy Townsend
5. Scott Minto
6. Barnsley and Spurs
7. Tore Andre Flo, Chris Sutton and Graeme Le Saux
8. Henning Berg
9. West Ham United
10. Marcel Desailly and Dennis Wise

QUIZ No. 29 - CHELSEA MANAGERS HAVE THEIR SAY
1. Tommy Docherty
2. Frank Lampard
3. Raffa Benitez
4. Danny Blanchflower
5. Jose Mourinho
6. Gianluca Vialli
7. Luiz Felipe Scolari
8. Claudio Ranieri
9. Ruud Gullit
10. Andre Villas-Boas on Gary Neville's criticism of David Luiz

QUIZ No. 30 - CHELSEA - SEASON 2000/01
1. Mario Melchiott
2. 23
3. Coventry City
4. Westerveld
5. Dennis Wise
6. Liverpool and Arsenal
7. Gianfranco Zola
8. Gudjohnsen and Gronkjaer
9. Charlton Athletic and Sunderland
10. Kevin Phillips

QUIZ No. 31 - CHELSEA - SEASON 2001/02
1. Sixth
2. Eidur Gudjohnsen
3. Marcel Desailly
4. Boudewijn Zenden
5. James Beattie
6. Jimmy-Floyd Hasselbaink and Mauricio Tarrico
7. West Ham United and Arsenal
8. John Terry
9. Spurs
10. Coventry City and Leeds United

QUIZ No. 32 - CHELSEA - SEASON 2002/03
1. Charlton Athletic
2. 5-0
3. Carlo Cudicini
4. Gianfranco Zola

5. John Terry
6. Shrewsbury Town and Stoke City
7. Frank Lampard
8. Carlton Cole
9. Everton
10. Liverpool and Steven Gerrard

QUIZ No. 33 - CHELSEA - SEASON 2003/04
1. Veron
2. Wolves
3. Lampard
4. Mutu
5. Scarborough
6. Arsenal and Aston Villa
7. Gudjohnsen
8. Portsmouth
9. Geremi
10. Leeds United

QUIZ No. 34 - CHELSEA - SEASON 2004/05
1. 95 points won and 15 goals conceded
2. Manchester City and Anelka
3. Damien Duff
4. Beattie
5. Lampard
6. Robben
7. Newcastle United
8. West Ham United and Fulham
9. The Valley – Charlton Athletic
10. Kezman

QUIZ No. 35 - CHELSEA - SEASON 2005-06
1. Charlton Athletic
2. Robert Huth
3. Asier Del Horno and Michael Essien
4. Carlton and Joe Cole
5. Carvalho own goal
6. John Terry
7. West Ham United
8. Ricardo Gardner and Stelios Giannakopoulos
9. Middlesbrough and Wigan Athletic
10. Frank Lampard

QUIZ No. 36 - CHELSEA - SEASON 2006/07
1. Drogba
2. Shevchenko
3. Hasselbaink
4. Watford
5. Arsenal and Reading
6. Wright-Phillips
7. Blackburn Rovers
8. Macclesfield
9. Ballack
10. Jon-Obi Mikel

QUIZ No. 37 – CHELSEA – SEASON 2007/08

1. Won 12, Drew 7, Lost 0
2. Lampard
3. Manchester City
4. Spurs
5. Barnsley
6. West Ham United and Derby County
7. Liverpool and Everton
8. Belletti
9. Gallas
10. The sack

QUIZ No. 38 – CHELSEA – SEASON 2008/09

1. Spurs
2. Anelka
3. Hull City
4. Gus Hiddink – the Russian national team
5. Burnley
6. Anelka and Drogba
7. Manchester City and Everton
8. Middlesbrough and Sunderland
9. Salomon Kalou
10. Stoke City

QUIZ No. 39 – CHELSEA – SEASON 2009/10

1. AC Milan
2. Ballack and Belletti
3. Ivanovic
4. Zenden and Sunderland
5. Aston Villa
6. Kalou
7. Wigan Athletic
8. Parker
9. Watford
10. Blackburn Rovers

QUIZ No. 40 – CHELSEA – SEASON 2010/11

1. 6-0 – Wigan and West Brom
2. Cech and Cole, (Ashley)
3. Aston Villa
4. Bosingwa
5. Ipswich Town
6. Newcastle United
7. David Luiz
8. West Ham United
9. Essien
10. Ashley Cole

QUIZ No. 41 – CHELSEA – SEASON 2011/12

1. West Brom
2. West Brom had sacked him
3. Torres
4. Liverpool
5. Leicester and Spurs
6. Lampard
7. Bosingwa and Drogba

8. 6-1 – Torres
9. Dempsey
10. Cisse – Djibril and Papiss

QUIZ No. 42 – CHELSEA – SEASON 2012/13

1. Benitez
2. West Brom
3. Aston Villa and Ramires
4. 5-4 to Chelsea
5. Wolves
6. Moses
7. Cesar Azpilicueta
8. Spurs and QPR
9. Mata
10. Jon Walters

QUIZ No. 43 – CHELSEA – SEASON 2013/14

1. Sunderland
2. Swindon Town and Arsenal
3. Hazard
4. Oscar
5. Bardsley
6. Remy
7. Eto'o and Schurrle
8. Salah – Wenger's 1,000th game
9. Ba and Willian
10. Ivanovic

QUIZ No. 44 – CHELSEA – SEASON 2014/15

1. 1-1 – Southampton
2. Diego Costa
3. True – they let in nine
4. Lampard
5. Six
6. Bradford City
7. Willian and Fabregas
8. Ivanovic
9. Swansea City
10. Goodison – 6-3

QUIZ No. 45 – CHELSEA – SEASON 2015/16

1. Newcastle United and Norwich City
2. Leicester City
3. Remy
4. Manchester City
5. Pedro
6. Terry
7. Hutton
8. Steven Naismith and Sergio Aguero
9. Swansea City and Courtois
10. Drinkwater

QUIZ No. 46 – CHELSEA – SEASON 2016/17

1. Trick question – it was Chelsea
2. Brentford
3. Michy Batshuayi
4. Azpilicueta and Diego Costa
5. Aguero and Fernandinho

6. Romeu and Bertrand
7. Oscar
8. Capoue
9. Fabregas
10. Giroud

QUIZ No. 47 – CHELSEA – SEASON 2017/18

1. Fifth
2. Azpilicueta and Alonso
3. Alvaro Morata
4. Davide Zappacosta
5. Nathan Ake and Patrick Van Aanholt
6. Nottingham Forest
7. Rudiger
8. Pedro and Morata
9. Hull City
10. Arsenal and David Luiz

QUIZ No. 48 – CHELSEA – SEASON 2018/19

1. Leicester City
2. Pedro
3. Sturridge and Mata
4. Manchester City – 6-0
5. Azpilicueta
6. Ross Barkley
7. Gonzalo Higuain
8. True
9. Derby County and one of the own goals was scored by Tomori who was on loan there from Chelsea
10. West Ham United

QUIZ No. 49 – CHELSEA – SEASON 2019/20

1. Mason Mount
2. Tammy Abraham
3. Grimsby Town
4. Nottingham Forest
5. Pulisic
6. Maguire
7. Rudiger
8. Fernandinho and Luiz
9. Caballero and Hudson-Odoi
10. Anthony Taylor – he sent off Moses in the 2017 final as well

QUIZ No. 50 – CHELSEA – SEASON 2020/21

1. Luiz Felipe Scolari
2. Tiago Silva and 13 (2-5 home and 3-3 away)
3. Jorginho and James
4. Ziyech and Zouma in the first game and Azpilicueta and Alonso in the second
5. Barnsley
6. Spurs and Leicester City
7. Tammy Abraham
8. Kai Havertz
9. Jorginho – all seven came from the penalty spot
10. Southampton

QUIZ No. 51 – CRYPTIC CHELSEA – PART 1

1. Ken Armstrong
2. Phil Driver
3. Tommy Langley
4. Mick Brolly
5. Ian 'Chico' Hamilton
6. Tommy Baldwin
7. Alan Hudson
8. Gary Chivers
9. Eric Parsons
10. David Speedie

QUIZ No. 52 – CRYPTIC CHELSEA – PART 2

1. James Argue
2. Kevin Hitchcock
3. Kerry Dixon
4. Mike Harrison
5. Paddy Mulligan
6. Gianfranco Zola
7. John Dempsey
8. Eden Hazard
9. Roy Bentley
10. Barry Bridges

QUIZ No. 53 – CRYPTIC CHELSEA – PART 3

1. Oscar
2. Alan Dickens
3. Dennis Wise
4. Jon Harley
5. Victor Moses
6. Damien Duff
7. Keith Dublin
8. John Sparrow
9. Bill Garner
10. Tommy Knox

QUIZ No. 54 – CRYPTIC CHELSEA – PART 4

1. James Bowie
2. Keith Weller
3. Eddie Newton
4. Steve Sherwood
5. David Hay
6. Manu Petit
7. Stewart Houston
8. Kenny Swain
9. Stan and Steve Wicks
10. Bill Livingstone and Gary Stanley

QUIZ No. 55 – CRYPTIC CHELSEA – PART 5

1. Paul Furlong
2. Danny Drinkwater
3. Billy Gilmour
4. Tammy Abraham
5. Andy Townsend
6. Jack Harrow
7. Frank Upton
8. Andy Malcolm
9. John Compton
10. Ruben Loftus-Cheek

CALL YOURSELF A BLUES FAN?

QUIZ No. 56 – CUP CAPTAINS
1. Jack Harrow
2. Terry Venables
3. Ron Harris
4. Dennis Wise
5. John Terry
6. Frank Lampard
7. Cesar Azpilicueta
8. Gary Cahill
9. Marcel Desailly
10. False – Dennis Wise has

QUIZ No. 57 – 'DON'T QUOTE ME ON THAT'
1. Clough on Hoddle
2. Warnock on Mourinho
3. Speedie on Bates
4. Real Madrid and Makelele
5. Glenn Hoddle and Chris Sutton
6. John Spencer on Zola
7. Vinnie Jones on Gullit
8. Capello on Vialli
9. Matthew Harding on David Mellor
10. Luis Suarez about biting Ivanovic

QUIZ No. 58 FANS
1. Minnie Driver
2. Dennis Waterman and Rodney Bewes
3. Alec Stewart
4. John Major and Bill Clinton
5. Russell Grant
6. Nigella Lawson
7. Richard Attenborough and Phil Daniels
8. Sean Locke
9. Jason Statham
10. Jimmy White

QUIZ No. 59 FOOTBALLER OF THE YEAR
1. Sid Owen, George Best, Tony Book and Ian Rush
2. Eden Hazard and N'golo Kante
3. Scott Parker
4. John Terry
5. Frank Lampard
6. Eden Hazard
7. Clive Allen
8. Danny Blanchflower
9. Antonio Conte
10. Ruud Gullit and Andriy Shevchenko – both with AC Milan

QUIZ No. 60 FULHAM ROAD FAVOURITES No. 1 – ROY BENTLEY
1. Bristol
2. £11,000
3. Eight
4. Newcastle United and Everton
5. Wales
6. Huddersfield Town and Sheffield Wednesday
7. Highbury
8. Fulham and QPR
9. Blackpool
10. When he took the job they were Swansea Town and when he left they were Swansea City

QUIZ No. 61 FULHAM ROAD FAVOURITES No. 2 – PETER BONETTI
1. 600
2. 'The cat'
3. Manchester City
4. Denmark
5. One
6. The St. Louis Stars
7. 20
8. Arsenal
9. Dundee United
10. More – 102

QUIZ No. 62 FULHAM ROAD FAVOURITES No. 3 – DIDIER DROGBA
1. Newcastle United
2. £24 million
3. France, Turkey, China, Canada and America
4. Ivory Coast
5. Crystal Palace
6. PSG
7. Kerry Dixon
8. Stoke City
9. Sunderland and Leicester City
10. Spurs and Liverpool

QUIZ No. 63 FULHAM ROAD FAVOURITES No. 4 – HUGHIE GALLACHER
1. Airdrieonians
2. Newcastle United
3. £10,000
4. Manchester United
5. 24
6. Newcastle United and Manchester City
7. West Ham United
8. Leeds United
9. Derby County
10. Newcastle United, Notts County and Grimsby Town

QUIZ No. 64 FULHAM ROAD FAVOURITES No. 5 – JIMMY GREAVES
1. White Hart Lane
2. Portsmouth
3. Scored more goals than he played games
4. Hillsborough
5. Preston North End
6. Wolves and West Brom
7. Newcastle United
8. Peru

9. Bradford Park Avenue and Millwall
10. Nottingham Forest and AC Milan

QUIZ No. 65 FULHAM ROAD FAVOURITES No. 6 – RON HARRIS

1. Chopper
2. He was the youngest player to captain a team in an FA Cup final
3. Sheffield Wednesday
4. 800
5. Four
6. 'I'm sorry, I thought you were Ron Harris'
7. West Ham United and Spurs
8. Burnley and Oldham Athletic
9. Brentford
10. Aldershot

QUIZ No. 66 FULHAM ROAD FAVOURITES No. 7 – EDEN HAZARD

1. Lille
2. Wigan Athletic and Reading
3. Newcastle United
4. Three
5. England
6. Crystal Palace
7. Cardiff City
8. Watford
9. Arsenal
10. Azerbaijan

QUIZ No. 67 FULHAM ROAD FAVOURITES No. 8 – FRANK LAMPARD

1. David Platt, Bryan Robson and Steven Gerrard
2. 2001 – £11 million
3. Newcastle United
4. A – Bobby Charlton
5. Nat Lofthouse and Gary Lineker
6. He had to take the kick three times due to encroachment
7. Bobby Tambling and Aston Villa
8. Bolton Wanderers
9. Swansea City, Manchester City and New York City
10. David Calderhead, Tommy Docherty, Glenn Hoddle, Claudio Ranieri and Antonio Conte

QUIZ No. 68 FULHAM ROAD FAVOURITES No. 9 – PETER OSGOOD

1. 'Osgood is good!'
2. Three
3. Emlyn Hughes
4. 1967/68
5. Italy
6. European Cup Winners' Cup
7. Crystal Palace
8. Jeff Astle
9. Norwich – three games
10. Eight

QUIZ No. 69 FULHAM ROAD FAVOURITES No. 10 – BOBBY TAMBLING

1. West Ham United
2. Workington
3. Sheffield
4. Eight
5. Charlton Athletic and Arsenal
6. Villa Park
7. Munich – against TSV Munchen 1860
8. West Bromwich Albion
9. Crystal Palace
10. 35

QUIZ No. 70 FULHAM ROAD FAVOURITES No. 11 – JOHN TERRY

1. Aston Villa
2. Nottingham Forest
3. Charlton Athletic and Crystal Palace
4. Schalke
5. Old Trafford and Steve McLaren
6. It was the first international goal in the 'new' Wembley
7. He went in goal after injuries to Cech and Cudicini and kept a clean sheet
8. Sunderland
9. Wembley
10. Fulham

QUIZ No. 71 FULHAM ROAD FAVOURITES No. 12 – GIANFRANCO ZOLA

1. Napoli
2. Ancelotti and Ranieri
3. Derby County
4. 1996/97
5. Liverpool and Wimbledon
6. Northern Ireland and England
7. Arrigo Sacchi and Maurizio Sarri
8. Arsenal – when playing for Parma
9. Liverpool
10. Juventus

QUIZ No. 72 GOALKEEPERS – PART 1

1. Bill Robertson
2. Dmitri Kharine
3. Henrique Hilario
4. John Phillips
5. Millwall and The Dell
6. Eddie Niedzwiecki
7. Frode Grodas
8. Peter Borota
9. Steve Francis
10. James Molyneux

QUIZ No. 73 GOALKEEPERS – PART 2

1. Reg Matthews
2. Ed de Goey
3. Thibaut Courtois
4. Harry Medhurst

5. Kepa Arrizabalaga
6. Mark Schwarzer
7. Carlo Cudicini
8. Bob Whiting and Jack Whitley
9. Rennes and Senegal
10. Sam Millington

QUIZ No. 74 GREENER GRASS (BEFORE)
1. Nicolas Anelka
2. Wayne Bridge
3. John Sissons
4. Glen Johnson
5. Dave Beasant
6. Olivier Giroud
7. Stan Crowther – for Aston Villa and Manchester United
8. Vinnie Jones and Dennis Wise
9. Micky Thomas and Mark Hughes
10. Cesc Fabregas and Glenn Hoddle

QUIZ No. 75 GREENER GRASS (AFTER)
1. Bobby Smith, Les Allen, Jimmy Greaves and Terry Venables
2. Chick Thomson
3. Peter Brabrook
4. Peter Osgood and Jim McCalliog
5. George Graham and Alan Hudson
6. Steve Sherwood
7. Jimmy-Floyd Hasselbaink – Cardiff City
8. Alex Stepney, Ray Wilkins, Juan Mata and Nemanja Matic
9. Pat Nevin
10. Nigel Spackman

QUIZ No. 76 HELPING HANDS (POST-WAR OWN GOALS)
1. Bert Trautmann
2. Tommy Docherty
3. Roy Paul
4. Albert Dunlop
5. Dave Pacey
6. Terry Neill
7. Pat Crerand
8. John Hollins
9. Sam Allardyce
10. Les Berry and Steve Cherry

QUIZ No. 77 HELPING HANDS (OWN GOALS IN THE PREMIER LEAGUE ERA)
1. Tim Howard, Chris Kirkland and Jussi Jaaskelainen
2. Richard Dunne
3. David Wheater
4. Steve Cook
5. Chris Smalling
6. Colin Hendry
7. Frank Sinclair
8. Emanuel Adebayor
9. Jonny Evans
10. Abel Xavier

QUIZ No. 78 IF THE CAP FITS – PART 1 – ENGLAND
1. Ken Armstrong and John Hollins
2. Roy Bentley
3. Dave Beasant
4. They all got three caps
5. Ken Shellito
6. Scott Parker
7. Cole – Ashley and Joe
8. Wayne Bridge and Barry Bridges
9. One
10. Ray Wilkins – at AC Milan

QUIZ No. 79 IF THE CAP FITS – PART 2 – SCOTLAND
1. False – his cap came at Aberdeen
2. Bobby Evans
3. David Speedie and John Spencer
4. Dundee and Crystal Palace
5. Gordon Durie
6. Steve Clarke
7. Everton and Tranmere Rovers
8. East Stirling
9. Craig Burley
10. Tommy Boyd

QUIZ No. 80 IF THE CAP FITS – PART 3 – WALES, NORTHERN IRELAND AND THE REPUBLIC OF IRELAND
1. Joey Jones – he won it with Liverpool in 1977
2. Kevin Wilson
3. Andy Townsend
4. Graham Moore
5. Seamus 'Jimmy' D'Arcy and Bill Dickson
6. Tony Cascarino
7. John Phillips and Eddie Niedzwiecki
8. Damien Duff
9. Ethan Ampadu
10. John Dempsey

QUIZ No. 81 IF THE CAP FITS – PART 4 – OVERSEAS PLAYERS
1. Norway
2. Spain
3. Germany
4. Bosnia
5. Nigeria
6. France
7. Romania
8. Denmark
9. USA
10. Argentina

QUIZ No. 82 IF THE CAP FITS – PART 5 – MORE OVERSEAS PLAYERS
1. Holland
2. Italy
3. Serbia
4. Australia
5. Morocco
6. Croatia

7. Brazil
8. Belgium
9. Portugal
10. Ivory Coast

QUIZ No. 83 MANAGERS
1. Steve Holland
2. Gianluca Vialli
3. Billy Birrell and Thomas Tuchel
4. True
5. Once – Dave Sexton – 1970
6. They've both provided six
7. Dave Sexton and Maurizio Sarri
8. Jose Mourinho and Gus Hiddink
9. Tommy Docherty
10. John Neal and Bobby Campbell

QUIZ No. 84 MULTIPLE CHOICE
1. A – Southampton
2. C – Leicester City
3. B – Liverpool
4. Arsenal
5. A – Newcastle United – 1906/07
6. D – Nottingham Forest
7. B – Terry
8. B – Ron Harris
9. C – 11
10. A – Keane

QUIZ No. 85 OPENING DAYS
1. Stockport County
2. Crespo
3. Burnley
4. Drogba
5. Preston North End
6. Dion Dublin
7. Bolton Wanderers
8. Glossop – George Hilsdon
9. Liverpool
10. Sunderland

QUIZ No. 86 OTHER COMPETITIONS
1. The FA Youth Cup
2. Manchester City and David Speedie
3. Middlesbrough and Tony Dorigo
4. Newcastle United and Everton
5. Charlton Athletic and Millwall
6. Eisenhower
7. Corinthians
8. Madrid and Monaco
9. Bayern Munich and Liverpool
10. Prague and Istanbul

QUIZ No. 87 POT LUCK
1. Southampton and Coventry City
2. Pedro
3. True
4. Didier Deschamps
5. Lillie Bridge – it hosted the 1873 final
6. Arsenal, Fulham, Liverpool and Manchester United
7. Brentford and QPR

8. Scoring Chelsea's first ever league goal
9. 1967 FA Cup final – Allan and Ron Harris
10. Mount Morris

QUIZ No. 88 STAMFORD BRIDGE
1. Athletics
2. Fulham
3. Hull City
4. Huddersfield Town
5. Arsenal
6. Austria
7. Tommy Lawton
8. Greyhound Racing
9. Archibald Leitch
10. Piccadilly

QUIZ No. 89 TRANSFERS - 1945-60
1. Tommy Lawton
2. Johnny McNichol
3. Sylvan Anderton
4. Les Stubbs
5. Eric Parsons
6. Brian Nicholas
7. Billy Gray
8. Johnny Brooks
9. Charlie Livesey
10. Tommy Walker

QUIZ No. 90 TRANSFERS - THE 1960s
1. West Ham United and Southampton
2. Aston Villa and Liverpool
3. Southampton and QPR
4. Sheffield United and Crystal Palace
5. Aston Villa and Arsenal
6. Celtic and Newport County
7. West Ham United and QPR
8. Derby County and back to the same club
9. West Brom and Manchester City
10. Arsenal and Torquay United

QUIZ No. 91 TRANSFERS - THE 1970s AND 1980s - PART 1
1. Aston Villa
2. Bristol City
3. Bournemouth
4. Crystal Palace
5. Leicester City
6. Darlington
7. Millwall
8. Clyde
9. Southend United
10. Hibernian

QUIZ No. 92 TRANSFERS - THE 1970s AND 1980s - PART 2
1. Aston Villa
2. Philadelphia Fury
3. Brentford
4. Swansea City
5. QPR

6. Dundee United
7. Crystal Palace
8. Oxford United
9. West Brom
10. Brighton and Hove Albion

QUIZ No. 93 TRANSFERS – THE 1990s – PART 1 – 'THE DOMESTIC SCENE'

1. Charlton Athletic
2. Watford
3. Rangers
4. Stoke City
5. Sheffield Wednesday
6. Newcastle United
7. Celtic
8. Swindon Town
9. Sheffield United
10. Norwich City

QUIZ No. 94 TRANSFERS – THE 1990s – PART 2 – 'THE FOREIGN LEGION'

1. Feyenoord
2. Anderlecht
3. Sampdoria
4. Juventus
5. AC Milan
6. Strasbourg
7. Parma
8. Real Zaragoza
9. Lazio
10. CSKA Moscow

QUIZ No. 95 TRANSFERS – 2000-20 – PART 1 – 'THE DOMESTIC SCENE'

1. Glen Johnson
2. Demba Ba
3. Scott Parker
4. Victor Moses
5. Yossi Benayoun
6. Ashley Cole and William Gallas
7. Damien Duff
8. Shaun Wright-Phillips and Daniel Sturridge
9. Wayne Bridge and Graeme Le Saux
10. Eider Gudjohnsen. Nicolas Anelka and Gary Cahill

QUIZ No. 96 TRANSFERS – THE 2000-20 – PART 2 – 'THE FOREIGN LEGION'

1. Valencia
2. Anderlecht
3. Fiorentina
4. Brondby
5. Bayern Munich
6. AC Milan
7. St. Etienne
8. Atletico Madrid
9. Napoli
10. Borussia Dortmund

QUIZ NO. 97 TRANSFERS – 2000-20 – PART 3 – 'MORE FOREIGN AFFAIRS'

1. Lyon
2. Roma
3. Real Madrid
4. Courtois and De Bruyne
5. Benfica
6. PSV Eindhoven
7. Ajax
8. Deco and Pedro
9. Paulo Ferreira and Ricardo Carvalho
10. Parma

QUIZ No. 98 TRUE OR FALSE

1. True
2. True
3. False – Damien Duff has 100 caps for the Republic of Ireland
4. True
5. True
6. False – Gordon Durie also did so
7. True
8. True
9. True
10. False – it was Lincoln City

QUIZ No. 99 VENUES

1. The Millennium Stadium
2. Old Trafford
3. Birmingham
4. Filbert Street
5. Bramall Lane and Leeds Road
6. Athens
7. Stockholm
8. Moscow and Munich
9. Amsterdam
10. Baku

QUIZ No. 100 'WEMBLEY – WEMBLEY!' – WINNING FA CUP SEMI-FINALS

1. Spurs
2. Newcastle United and Southampton
3. Fulham
4. Gavin Peacock and Gus Poyet
5. Watford and Spurs
6. Willian
7. Spurs
8. Didier Drogba and Florent Malouda
9. Villa Park, Old Trafford, Highbury and White Hart Lane
10. Harold Halse, Tony Hateley, Peter Houseman, Ian Hutchinson, Mark Hughes and Eden Hazard

BACK COVER QUESTION

Ted Drake, Danny Blanchflower, Geoff Hurst, David Webb, Ian Porterfield, Glenn Hoddle, Roberto Di Matteo and Frank Lampard are the eight managers, while the interim manager is Ray Wilkins. Tommy Docherty conceded the penalty in the 1954 final.